THE NOBLE GASES

THE NOBLE GASES

HOWARD H. CLAASSEN

CHAIRMAN OF SCIENCE DIVISION
WHEATON COLLEGE

D. C. HEATH AND COMPANY

Preface

The primary purpose of this book is to make the recent developments in the chemistry of the noble gases easily available to students. The first several chapters very briefly review those physical properties that relate most closely to chemistry, and the remainder of the book discusses compounds of the noble gases.

There are large differences between sections of the book in level of background needed for complete understanding. Chapters one, two, three, five, six, eight, and eleven are suitable for the freshman chemistry student, and do not depend on the other, more difficult sections. Chapters four and seven assume some knowledge of thermodynamics, and are most appropriate for students who have had a physical chemistry course. Chapters nine and ten are designed to challenge the best senior students; they include topics not usually covered in undergraduate textbooks or courses. For these, some detailed explanations are given, as well as references for background reading.

Several sections of the book are written in the style of a review paper, with frequent references to the original papers. This seems appropriate at this time when relatively few workers are involved and it is still possible to approach accuracy in giving credit fairly for the various contributions. It is not intended, however, to be complete in listing references. Rather, the purpose has been to list those that are most definitive and therefore most helpful to the student who needs more detailed information than given here.

The author is indebted to many sources of help. Wheaton College gave him a reduced teaching load for a semester to enable him to complete the major part of the manuscript. To Argonne National Laboratory he is grateful for the support that made possible his participation in some of the significant developments described and allowed him to write with first-hand familiarity on many of the topics. The Laboratory also furnished many of the illustrations in this book. To his colleagues at Argonne, Evan Appleman, Cedric L. Chernick, John G. Malm, Henry Selig, and others, the author owes thanks for reading parts of his manuscript, for keeping him informed about their work prior to publication, and for supplying up-to-date information on references to new publications. This help has made it possible to be current to the time of final revision of the manuscript as far as new developments are concerned. This is important because much of the work on the chemistry of the noble gases in 1962 and 1963 was hastily published in short notes, and a number of tentative conclusions that were incorrect have only recently been revised in more lengthy papers.

Howard H. Claassen

Contents

Chapter

1   *Historical—Discovery of the Noble Gases and the Sudden Tarnishing of their Nobility in 1962*   1

2   *Abundances and Physical Properties*   5

3   *Atomic Structure*   8

4   *Pressure-Density-Temperature Relationships and Interatomic Forces*   26

5   *Chemical Properties as Known Before 1962*   34

6   *Preparations of Many Compounds, 1962 and After*   37
     6–A   Xenon Fluorides   38
     6–B   Xenon Oxide-Fluorides, Oxides, Mixed Fluorides, and Chloride   43
     6–C   Krypton and Radon Fluorides   45
     6–D   Possible Compounds of the Lighter Noble Gases   48

7   *Thermochemistry of Xenon and Krypton Compounds*   50

8   *Solution Chemistry*   60
     8–A   Anhydrous Hydrogen Fluoride Solutions   60
     8–B   Hydrolysis Reactions   61
     8–C   Xenon Oxy-Acids and Their Salts   64

9   *Structural Studies*   71
     9–A   Theory of Molecular Vibrations   71
     9–B   Structures of XeF_2 and KrF_2 79
     9–C   Structures of XeF_4 and $XeOF_4$ 84
     9–D   Structure of XeF_6 92
     9–E   Structure of $XeF_2 \cdot XeF_4$ 94
     9–F   Structure of XeO_3 94
     9–G   Structure of XeO_4 95
     9–H   Structure of Metal Perxenates   96

10   *Chemical Binding and Theoretical Descriptions of Xenon Compounds*   98

11   *Conclusion*   111

Historical—Discovery of the Noble Gases and the Sudden Tarnishing of their Nobility in 1962

The periodic table of the elements that Mendeleeff published in 1871 is basically similar to a modern table. Although elements are missing here and there, the most noticeable omission is the whole column that in a modern table appears at the extreme right. The six elements now listed in this column are called the rare, inert, or noble gases of the atmosphere. Argon, the most plentiful of these, was isolated and announced as a new element in 1894 by Lord Rayleigh (John W. Strutt) and Sir William Ramsey. More than a century earlier, Henry Cavendish had combined oxygen and nitrogen from air by electrical sparking to form nitrous acid. He observed that "a small bubble of air remained unabsorbed," and wrote that if there was an inert part of the air different from nitrogen it was less than 1/120 part of the whole. This observation was apparently forgotten and the possibility of an unknown constituent of air came up again much later in a new context. Lord Rayleigh found that nitrogen obtained by removal of the other known gases of the atmosphere was measurably more dense than nitrogen prepared from chemical sources such as ammonia. He and Ramsey undertook a collaborative effort to explain this discrepancy. They were able to isolate a heavy fraction of air that was more inert than nitrogen, and they announced at the August, 1894 meeting of the British Association that a one percent fraction of the atmosphere seemed to be completely inert and had a definite and characteristic discharge spectrum quite different from that of nitrogen.

In his November, 1894, Anniversary Address, Lord Kelvin, president of the Royal Society, stated that the discovery of a new, inert constituent of the atmosphere was undoubtedly the greatest scientific achievement of the year. He emphasized that this work of Rayleigh and Ramsey was another instance showing the importance of precise measurement. Nothing had appeared in print as yet on the subject but it was announced that Ramsey would read a detailed paper at the Royal Society the following January. For that meeting a crowd of over eight hundred assembled to hear him (the full text in *Philosophical Transactions* is fifty-four pages). This was the largest crowd to attend a meeting in the history of the society.

The paper described his many efforts to form compounds of the new element using various chemical reagents. The failure of all of these thoroughly established the chemical inertness and suggested the name argon (the lazy one). But placing the new element in the periodic table presented real difficulties. From gas density measurement, the molecular weight was known to be approximately 40, but the nature of the molecules was not easy to establish because of lack of compounds. Rayleigh and Ramsey reported that measurements of the velocity of sound in the gas gave a value of 1.66 for the ratio of specific heats, C_p/C_v. Classical theories of equipartition of energy predicted for this ratio values of 1.67, 1.40, and lower for monatomic, diatomic, and polyatomic molecules, respectively. They therefore concluded that argon was monatomic. Although mercury vapor had earlier been established as monatomic by such a measurement, and though it now seems natural that an inert element would not form molecules, the discussion which followed the paper was mainly concerned with skepticism on this point. A monatomic gas meant an atomic weight of 40 and this should place the element between potassium and calcium, or between calcium and scandium. Without knowledge of isotopes it was not easy to recognize that argon could precede potassium even though its atomic weight was greater. A more detailed account of this work on argon is given by Hiebert (1).

Within the next five years, all five other noble gases known today were isolated and characterized, and a new column was established for them in the periodic table. The yellow spectral line of the lightest of them had been observed in 1868 in the spectrum of the sun's chromosphere and the solar element named helium. This was the next of the noble gases to be isolated, in 1895. It was obtained from a uranium ore by heating. Krypton, neon, and xenon were isolated from air, and finally radon isotopes were found in 1900 as emanations from naturally radioactive elements.

Through the following decades the early reputation of this new family of elements for inertness or nobility was doubted occasionally by chemists, and some of them reported evidences for compound formation. The claims, however, were all short-lived since either the investigators later found errors in their observations, or other workers could not duplicate their results. The legend that the inert gases do not form stable compounds was rather firmly established chemical dogma until the spring of 1962. At that time Neil Bartlett at the University of British Columbia had found that gaseous oxygen could be oxidized by the vapor of PtF_6. He gave evidence for the existence of an ionic compound, $(O_2)^+(PtF_6)^-$. Next he noted that the ionization potential of xenon atoms is almost identical to that of oxygen molecules, and tried mixing xenon gas with PtF_6 vapor. The result was instantaneous reaction to form a solid product that he identified as $Xe^+(PtF_6)^-$. This was reported in a short note that appeared in the *Proceedings of the Chemical Society* in the summer of 1962.

A group that was studying fluorine chemistry at the Argonne National Laboratory took keen interest in this note, primarily because two of them, John Malm and the author, together with Bernard Weinstock, had first prepared PtF_6 in 1957. That was the first hexavalent compound of platinum. Samples of PtF_6 were on hand at Argonne, and Bartlett's experiment was immediately repeated and extended to include a similar reaction between xenon and RuF_6 by Cedric Chernick, Henry Selig, and John Malm. Part of the reason for the interest at Argonne stemmed from first-hand knowledge that these unstable hexafluorides were very powerful fluorinating agents. They had often been observed to fluorinate materials that were immune to fluorine, itself. There was, therefore, a suspicion that in Bartlett's reaction might be included formation of covalent bonds between xenon and fluorine rather than only a removal of a xenon electron.

Henry Selig, John Malm, and the author experimented by heating a mixture of xenon and fluorine gases. The result was a stable compound, xenon tetrafluoride, in one hundred percent yield with respect to xenon. The result of this experiment quickly became widely known, and many chemists began to experiment with xenon compounds. Interest was so wide that a special meeting on noble-gas compounds was arranged at Argonne seven months after the first preparation of xenon tetrafluoride. The papers presented there came from as far away as Yugoslavia and more than one hundred different authors were represented. The published version of these papers (2), came to nearly 400 pages. The major part of the present volume is devoted to these developments since August, 1962. Before that year a book on the noble gases would not have been of great interest to most chemists.

References

1. E. N. HIEBERT, pages 3 to 20, "Noble-Gas Compounds," H. H. HYMAN, Ed., Univ. of Chicago Press, 1963.
2. "Noble-Gas Compounds," H. H. HYMAN, Ed., Univ. of Chicago Press, 1963.

CHAPTER **2**

Abundance and Physical Properties

The atmosphere contains all six of the noble gases in measurable amounts and is the source used by commercial suppliers for all but helium and radon. Table II.1 lists concentrations given by Glueckauf and Kitt (1) and the atomic masses given for the international committee on atomic weights by Cameron and Wichers (2). Helium, argon, and radon are known to be produced in the earth as products from naturally occurring radioactive minerals. Helium can escape

Table II.1

The Noble Gases in the Atmosphere

Gas	Concentration by Volume in Parts per Million	Atomic Mass
He	5.239 ± .004	4.0026
Ne	18.18 ± .04	20.183
Ar	9340.	39.948
Kr	1.139 ± .01	83.80
Xe	0.086 ± .001	131.30
Rn	6×10^{-14}	(222)

from the upper atmosphere because of its low atomic mass and radon decays with a short lifetime, and so these may be present in equilibrium concentration. The amount of argon, however, is increasing, as it is produced by the β-decay of potassium-40. Argon is so plentiful

5

compared to the others that a sample of noble gases obtained from air by removal of all other constituents is 99.7% argon. Xenon, the most rare of the stable ones, is still plentiful enough that a penny for every xenon atom in a cubic centimeter of air would easily make one the richest man in the world.

Helium is commercially obtained from natural gas wells in the southwestern United States. The concentration of helium in this gas is between one and six mole percent. Separation plants liquefy the main constituents of the gas and then purify the helium that is in the gas phase. The longest-lived isotope of radon, Rn-222, has a half-life of 3.82 days. It is the only gaseous daughter product in the radium decomposition chain, and so it is collected by pumping on radium salts.

In the United States, neon, argon, krypton, and xenon are obtained in adequate supply as by-products from air reduction plants in which oxygen is produced by distillation of liquefied air. Neon is concentrated to about 2% in a gaseous nitrogen fraction, and argon to about 12% in a gaseous oxygen fraction. Further concentration is accomplished by separate neon and argon recovery columns and purification by adsorption or catalytic combustion processes. Krypton and xenon, since they are both much less volatile than nitrogen, tend to concentrate in a liquid fraction in the oxygen plant. The noble gases are then separated by fractional distillation.

Some of the most common physical properties of the noble gases and their liquid or solid phases are given in Table II.2.

References

1. E. GLUECKAUF, "Compendium of Meteorology," American Meteorologic Society, Boston, 1951.
   E. Glueckauf and G. P. Kitt, *Proc. Roy. Soc.* (London), **A234,** 557, (1956).
2. A. E. CAMERON and E. WITHERS, *J. Am. Chem. Soc.*, **84,** 4175 (1962).
3. J. A. BEATTIE, Chap. VIII of "Argon, Helium and the Rare Gases," G. A. COOK, Ed., Interscience, 1961.
4. A. C. H. HALLETT, Chap. IX of "Argon, Helium and the Rare Gases," *ibid.*
5. A. C. JENKINS, Chap. X of "Argon, Helium and the Rare Gases," *ibid.*
6. Calculated, assuming ideal gases and sound velocity measurements: He— W. G. SCHNEIDER and G. J. Thiessen, *Can. J. Res.* **28A,** 509 (1950); Ne—A. VAN ITTERBEEK and L. THYS, *Physica*, **5,** 889 (1938); Ar—A. VAN ITTERBEEK and O. V. PAEMEL, *Physica*, **5,** 845 (1938).

Table II.2

Summary of Physical Properties

Elements / Properties	He	Ne	Ar	Kr	Xe	Rn	Ref.
Gas Density at 0°C and 1 Atm (g/liter)	0.17850	0.90002	1.78380	3.7493	5.8971	—	3
Liquid Density at the Boiling Point (g/cm³)	.1249	1.207	1.388	2.413	3.06	—	4
Solid Density at the Triple Point (g/cm³)	—	1.444	1.623	2.826	3.540	—	4
Boiling Point (°C)	−268.935	−246.08	−185.88	−153.4	−108.12	−62	4
Triple Point (°C)	none	−248.60	−189.37	−157.20	−111.9	−71	4
Critical Temperature (°C)	−267.9	−228.7	−122.3	−63.8	16.59	105	5
Critical Pressure (atm)	2.26	26.9	48.3	54.3	57.64	62	5
Critical Density (g/cm³)	0.0693	0.484	0.536	0.908	1.100	—	5
Ratio of heat capacities, C_p/C_v, −5 to +20°C	1.672	1.677	1.667	—	—	—	6
Refractive Index at 1 Atm and 20°C, n_D	1.000035	1.000067	1.000284	1.000427	1.000702	—	5
Dielectric Constants at 25°C and 1 Atm	1.0000639	1.0001229	1.0005085	1.000768	1.001238	—	5
Viscosity at 20°C, (micropoises)	196.14	313.81	222.86	249.55	227.40	229.0	5
Solubility in Water at 1 Atm Gas Pressure, (Cm³) of STP Gas/Kg Water)							5
At 0°C	9.78	14.0	52.4	99.1	203.2	—	
At 20°C	8.61	10.5	33.6	59.4	108.1	—	
At 30°C	8.42	9.89	28.5	48.8	85.4	—	

CHAPTER **3**

Most of our common gases consist of diatomic or polyatomic molecules, but the noble gases consist of monatomic molecules. Modern quantum mechanics has provided a fairly detailed description of the nature and sizes of atoms. Before discussing this, however, it will be instructive to consider some of the more classical models of atoms and to discuss a few of the indirect methods of determining the sizes of atoms.

One of these methods depends on dielectric constant measurements for a gas. These may be used to calculate atomic radii if a suitable model of the atom is assumed. The dielectric constant, K, of an insulating material may be defined as the ratio, C^1/C, where C^1 and C are the electrical capacitances of a given capacitor with the material, and with a vacuum, respectively, between the plates. C^1 is always greater than C because the atoms of the material are distorted (or the molecules are aligned) by the electric field of the capacitor, and contribute fields of their own. The average effect of the molecules is to weaken the field and this reduces the potential difference for a given charge on the plates, and thus increases the capacitance, since $Q = CV$.

To calculate the size of this effect the concept of dipole moment is used. This concept is most useful for a localized group of charges including equal amounts of positive and negative charge such as makes up an atom or molecule. It is defined as

$$\mathbf{p} = \int \mathbf{r}dq \qquad (1)$$

8

Where **r** is the vector from some arbitrary origin of coordinates to the point where the small bit of charge, dq, is located, and the integral is over all the space where the charges that make up the dipole are found. As an example, consider the simplest case of two point charges, $+q$ and $-q$, separated by a small distance, a, and shown in Fig. 3.1. For this the integral of Eq. (1) becomes a sum of two terms, $\mathbf{p} = \mathbf{r}(-q) + \mathbf{r}_2(q)$, or $\mathbf{p} = q(\mathbf{r}_2 - \mathbf{r}_1)$. Since $(\mathbf{r}_2 - \mathbf{r}_1)$ is a vector of length, a, from the negative to the positive charge, the result is independent of the location of the origin, O. The dipole moment of a pair of equal and opposite point charges is thus equal to qa, and is a vector pointing from the negative toward the positive charge.

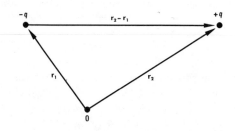

Figure 3.1   A dipole consisting of two equal and opposite charges.

The polarization of a dielectric on a macroscopic scale is specified by the vector **P**, defined as the total dipole moment per unit volume. In the case of spherical atoms of a monatomic gas in an electric field, the dipole moments induced by the field are all parallel, and $P = np$, where n is the number of atoms per unit volume. The electric displacement vector is related to the electric field vector, **E**, by the relation (using M.K.S. units)

$$\mathbf{D} = \epsilon_0\mathbf{E} + \mathbf{P} \tag{2}$$

where ϵ_0 is the permittivity of free space.

In a parallel-plate capacitor of area A and spacing s between the plates, $Q = DA$ and $V = Es$, where Q is the total charge on one plate and V is the potential difference between the plates. Then

$$C^1 = Q/V = DA/Es = (\epsilon_0 E + P)A/Es \tag{3}$$

When there is a vacuum between the plates, P is zero, so

$$K = C^1/C = 1 + \frac{P}{\epsilon_0 E} = 1 + \frac{np}{\epsilon_0 E} \tag{4}$$

9

Simple models may then be used to relate the radius of an atom to the ratio, p/E and thus to the dielectric constant by Eq. (4). Two such models will be discussed.

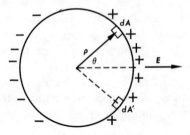

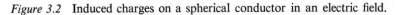

Figure 3.2   Induced charges on a spherical conductor in an electric field.

First, perhaps the simplest assumption for this purpose is that "closed-shell" or noble-gas atoms behave in an electric field like conducting spheres.   Such spheres are positively charged on one hemisphere and negatively charged on the other, and therefore have a dipole moment.   Figure 3.2 shows a sphere with charges induced by a uniform electric field.   It can be shown (see, for example, p. 76 in Reference 1) that the charge density on the surface of the sphere is

$$\sigma = 3\epsilon_0 E \cos\theta \qquad (5)$$

where E is the field there would be if the sphere were not there. The charges induced on the sphere of course distort the field locally. From Eqs. (1) and (5), the dipole moment is

$$\mathbf{p} = \int \mathbf{r}\, dq = \int \rho\sigma\, dA = 3\epsilon_0 E \int \rho \cos\theta\, dA \qquad (6)$$

where the integration is over the surface of the sphere.   Since this is a vector integration it must be done by components.   The components of $\mathbf{p}$ perpendicular to $\mathbf{E}$ will integrate to zero since the contributions of area elements like dA and dA' will cancel.   Thus, $\mathbf{p}$ will point in the direction of $\mathbf{E}$ and will have the magnitude

$$p = 3\epsilon_0 E \int \rho \cos\theta \cos\theta\, dA = 3\epsilon_0 E \iint \rho \cos^2\theta\rho\, d\theta\rho \sin\theta\, d\phi$$

$$= 4\pi\epsilon_0 E\rho^3 \qquad (7)$$

Here θ and ϕ are the usual spherical coordinates and dA has been replaced by $\rho\, d\theta\rho \sin\theta\, d\phi$.   The limits of integration are 0 to π for θ and 0 to 2π for ϕ.   The result (7) may be written $p/E = 4\pi\epsilon_0\rho^3$.

The second simple model of the atom pictures the positive nucleus at the center of a negatively charged sphere of uniform charge density. Distortion in an electric field consists of a shift of the center of the negative charge away from the positive charge to give a dipole. Figure 3.3 pictures such a model with an electric field to the right so that the center of the negative sphere is a distance x to the left of the nucleus, of charge $+ Ze$ where Z is the atomic number. Considering the heavy nucleus as fixed, we may equate the two forces on the negative sphere. One is simply $Eq = EZe$ toward the left, and the other is the force of attraction between the nucleus and the negative sphere. This latter may be simply calculated, if it is remembered that a uniform spherical shell of charge behaves as if it were concentrated at the center for points outside the sphere, and has a net effect of zero at any point inside the sphere. Thus, all the negative charge inside the dashed sphere of Figure 3.3, $Ze(x^3/\rho^3)$, may be considered as if it were concentrated at the center, and all the negative charge between the dashed and solid spheres may be ignored. Equating the forces yields

$$EZe = \frac{(Ze)^2(x^3/\rho^3)}{4\pi\epsilon_0 x^2} \qquad (8)$$

or

$$\frac{Zex}{E} = p/E = 4\pi\epsilon_0\rho^3 \qquad (9)$$

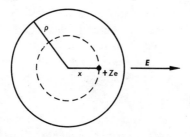

Figure 3.3 The rigid sphere of negative charge with center displaced from the nucleus.

Perhaps surprisingly, this result is the same as that given by the first model. Substitution of Eq. (7) or Eq. (9) into Eq. (4) yields

$$K = 1 + 4\pi n\rho^3 \qquad (10)$$

a relation between dielectric constant and atomic radii.

Another classical approach to the determination of atomic sizes makes use of the van der Waals equation, an early and famous equation of state for gases that fits measured data over a wider range of the variables than does the ideal gas equation. An ideal gas may be thought of as a collection of a very large number of atoms whose sizes are very small compared to their average separation distances, and that exert no forces on each other except when they collide. For such a gas, it is easily shown that the pressure exerted on the walls of a container of volume V is

$$p = Nm\overline{u^2}/3V \tag{11}$$

Where N is the number of atoms, m is the mass of one and $\overline{u^2}$ is the average value of the squares of the speeds of the molecules. With the assumption that temperature, T, is proportioned to $m\overline{u^2}/2$, the average kinetic energy per molecule, this may be written

$$pv = RT \tag{12}$$

where v is the molar volume and R is the general gas constant.

Clausius first improved this equation so as to allow for the finite sizes of atoms. If the atoms are considered as hard spheres of radii ρ, two atoms at the instant of a collision have their centers separated by a distance 2ρ. If we consider the space available for one atom to move around in, we may think, for the moment, of this atom as a point and of all others as having radii 2ρ. The center of the one atom is excluded from a spherical volume, $4\pi(2\rho)^3/3$, around each of the other spheres. Actually this should be divided by two, since only the hemisphere on the side of approach is effective in the exclusion. For a mole of gas, with N_0 atoms, the effective volume is not v, but $v - b$, where the excluded volume

$$b = N_0 4\pi(2\rho)^3/(3)(2) = 16N_0\pi\rho^3/3 \tag{13}$$

Van der Waals made a further change to allow for small attractive forces between the atoms. The force per unit area exerted on the walls, or p, would be somewhat less than indicated by Eq. (11) because of intermolecular attractions. The amount it would be diminished would depend on the density. Van der Waals reasoned that it would be proportional to the square of the density because the amount of attractive force on a given small volume of gas is proportioned to the number of atoms in that volume, but also to the number of atoms in the remainder of the space that exert the attraction.

Since molar volume, v, is inversely proportional to density, the diminution in pressure is a/v^2, where a is a constant. The van der Waals equation is thus

$$\left(p + \frac{a}{v^2}\right)(v - b) = RT \qquad (14)$$

where a and b are constants characteristic of a given gas. By means of Eq. (13) and Eq. (14), atomic radii may be calculated. The values of a and b for a given gas are usually obtained from measurements of critical temperature and pressure.

The critical temperature of a gas is that temperature above which it is not possible to liquefy the gas by application of pressure. This may be clarified by the p-v diagram of Fig. 3.4. The solid curves represent constant temperature processes, or isotherms. At the high temperature, T_1, the isotherm is very nearly an hyperbola represented by $pv = $ constant. For a low temperature like T_3, however, a decrease in volume produces liquefaction beginning at the point B, and the horizontal line AB represents an equilibrium between liquid and vapor. At A there is only liquid, and pressure rises very steeply with further compression. At temperatures above T_3 the liquid-vapor line, e.g., $A'B'$, shortens until, at the critical temperature, and above, no liquid appears at all.

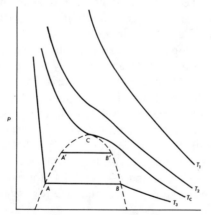

Figure 3.4 Isotherms for a typical pure substance below and above the critical temperature.

The van der Waals equation can be fit rather well to a curve like T_2 in Fig. 3.4. It has been used even for the critical isotherm. This curve is evidently horizontal, and also has a point of inflection at C.

13

Thus, both the first and the second derivative of p with respect to v at the constant temperature, T_c, must equal zero. If Eq. (14) is solved for p and the first and second derivatives are set equal to zero with $T = T_c$, the two equations may be solved for a and b. The result is

$$b = v_c/3 \tag{15}$$

and

$$a = 9Rv_cT_c/8 \tag{16}$$

where the subscript, c, has been added to indicate critical volume and temperature. Since it is easier to measure critical pressures and temperatures than volumes, Eqs. (15) and (16) may be substituted back into Eq. (14) to give

$$b = \frac{RT_c}{8p_c} \tag{17}$$

This, with Eq. (13) may be used to determine atomic radii from critical pressures and temperatures.

Another approach involves measurements of gas viscosity to gain some information on how rapidly molecules are transported from one location to another, and thus, again with use of suitable models, on collision diameters. To discuss this we begin with a definition of the concept of viscosity. If two surfaces of solid bodies are kept parallel to each other and a constant distance apart, but one of them is moving relative to the other, a fluid filling the space between will exert a frictional drag. This frictional retarding force is found by experiment to be proportional directly to the velocity of the motion and to the area of the surface and inversely to the distance between the surfaces. A liquid fluid may be visualized as composed of many thin layers that slide over neighboring layers, so that the liquid near the stationary surface has zero velocity, successive layers have successively greater velocities, and the final layer next to the moving surface moves with that surface. Figure 3.5 indicates two layers of fluid of thickness, dy, and area, A, for which the velocities from top to bottom are $u + du$, u, and $u - du$. The force required to overcome the frictional drag is proportional to $A(du)/(dy)$, or

$$F = \eta A \frac{du}{dy} \tag{18}$$

This equation defines η, the coefficient of viscosity. If cgs units are used, η has dimensions of dyne sec cm^{-2}, and this is named the poise.

For liquids, the viscosity generally decreases with increasing tem-

14

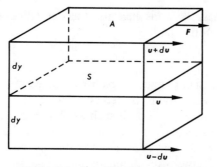

Figure 3.5 Laminar flow of a fluid.

perature. Water, for example, at 20°C and 100°C has viscosities of 0.010 and 0.0030 poises, respectively. For gases, however, the viscosity always rises with rise in temperature. Air at 0°C, one atmosphere, and 100°C, one atmosphere, has viscosity of 0.000133 and 0.000245 poises, respectively. Since the molecules are relatively far apart for gases, there can be no frictional drag in the sense of molecules sliding across one another. Rather, the drag is due to molecules diffusing from one layer to another and the momentum they carry across. With reference to Fig. 3.5, if molecules of average velocity **u** from the bottom of the layer diffuse upward to the top of the layer, their average velocity to the right must increase. Thus a force to the right must be supplied. The rate of diffusion is dependent on collision diameters, and so viscosity can be related to atomic radii.

If the atoms of a gas are considered to have definite radii, ρ, the number of collisions that one of them encounters in time t may be taken as $4\pi\rho^2\bar{v}nt$, where $\bar{v}$ is the average speed and n the number of atoms per unit volume. This is obtained by considering that the atom travels a total distance, $\bar{v}t$, and collides with any others whose centers are inside a cylinder of length, $\bar{v}t$ and radius, 2ρ. The number in this cylinder is n times the volume of the cylinder. The average distance that the atom travels between collisions λ is the distance moved in time t divided by the number of collisions, or

$$\lambda = 1/4\pi\rho^2 n \qquad (19)$$

This reasoning, and the result, is only approximately correct, however, since all the other molecules are moving also, and some of them may come into the cylinder, imagined above, from the side, to collide with the given molecule. Taking account of the various speeds and directions of motion of all the molecules is rather involved. Kennard (2),

15

for example, may be consulted for the derivation of the correct formula for mean free path

$$\lambda = 1/\sqrt{24}\pi\rho^2 n \tag{20}$$

which is smaller than the above result by the factor $1/\sqrt{2}$.

To calculate viscosity it is necessary to consider at what rate molecules are crossing a surface such as S in Fig. 3.5, and how far they move perpendicular to S on the average before colliding. To obtain this average, it is necessary to consider not only the mean free path, λ, but the distribution of individual free paths, and to average out all possible directions of molecular motions. Sears (3) shows how this process leads to $n\bar{v}/4$ for the number crossing a plane like S from each side per unit area per unit time, and to $\frac{2}{3}\lambda$ for the average perpendicular distance from S where the molecules crossing S made their last collision before crossing.

At a distance $\frac{2}{3}\lambda$ above the plane S, the flow velocity is

$$u + \tfrac{2}{3}\lambda \frac{du}{dy}$$

and the momentum of a molecule with this velocity is the mass, m, times this velocity. Multiplying by $n\mathbf{v}/4$, the number crossing per unit area per unit time, gives

$$\tfrac{1}{4}n\bar{v}m\left(u + \tfrac{2}{3}\lambda \frac{du}{dy}\right)$$

for the net rate at which momentum is carried across the plane per unit area per unit time by those atoms crossing from above. For those crossing from below the corresponding rate is

$$\tfrac{1}{4}n\bar{v}m\left(u - \tfrac{2}{3}\lambda \frac{du}{dy}\right)$$

The difference between these two

$$\tfrac{1}{3}n\bar{v}m\lambda \frac{du}{dy}$$

is the net rate of momentum transfer per unit area per unit time. This, by Newton's second law, must equal the force per unit area, or

$$\tfrac{1}{3}n\bar{v}m\lambda \frac{du}{dy} = \frac{F}{A} \tag{21}$$

From Eq. (18), Eq. (20) and Eq. (21) we obtain

$$\eta = \frac{m\bar{v}}{3\sqrt{24\pi\rho}^{\,2}} \qquad (22)$$

The mean speed of molecules is $\sqrt{8kT/\pi m}$ (Ref. 3, p. 236), and so we have

$$\eta = \sqrt{\pi mkT}/6\pi^2\rho^2 \qquad (23)$$

as another relation between a measurable property of a gas and the radii of its atoms. Here k is Boltzmann's constant, which is the general gas constant divided by Avogadro's number.

The final classical method of determination of atomic radii for the noble gases to be mentioned involves the separation of atoms in the solid state at very low temperatures. It is known from quantum mechanics that even at absolute zero of temperature the atoms of a crystal are not stationary. They have what is called "zero-point" vibrational energy, which must mean some vibrational motion. For the noble gases, however, with the possible exception of helium, this will be very small, and we may take the closest distance between atom centers in the crystal at very low temperatures as a reasonable value of atomic diameters. Neon, argon, krypton, and xenon all crystallize in the face-centered cubic structure. The unit cell dimension a and the atomic radius ρ, as defined in this way, are related by $a^2 = 8\rho^2$. This may be seen by reference to Fig. 3.6. The value of ρ may thus be simply calculated from the low temperature x-ray data.

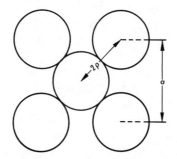

Figure 3.6   One face of the face-centered cubic unit cell.

Before presenting the results obtained by means of these various classical methods for atomic radii, we take up the question of what modern quantum mechanics can tell us about the nature and sizes of atoms. We begin with the model of the hydrogen atom introduced

17

by Niels Bohr in 1913, that could explain all the main features of the emission and absorption spectra of atomic hydrogen and hydrogenlike atoms like ionized helium, doubly ionized lithium, etc. The model was basically an electron orbiting around a massive nucleus in the inverse square electric field according to the laws of classical mechanics and electrodynamics, except for a few *ad hoc* departures. One was the restriction of angular momenta to integral multiples of $h/2\pi$, with sudden "jumps" from one value to another. Accompanying these "jumps" were energy changes that were radiated or absorbed as quanta of light of energy hf, where h is the constant introduced earlier by Planck, and f is the frequency of the light, considered classically as a wave. A further assumption was that, contrary to classical theory, the electron circulating in an orbit did not radiate energy.

The spectacular success of the Bohr theory in explaining known spectra and in predicting new spectral lines inspired great effort to extend the theory to atoms of more than one electron. Many suggestions were made for neutral helium atoms with two electrons, but none of these produced calculated results in agreement with observed spectra.

Over a period of about twenty years, however, a powerful and comprehensive theory was built up by Bohr, de Broglie, Heisenberg, Dirac, Schroedinger, and others, called quantum mechanics or quantum electrodynamics. In using the Schroedinger form of this theory, if one knows analytic functions for the kinetic and potential energies of a system, one can write down a partial differential equation for a wave function, usually designated by ψ. Of the many solutions of such equations only certain ones, called well-behaved, are taken to have physical meaning. This selection among possible solutions gives rise rather naturally to quantum numbers and to discrete possible values of energy, angular momentum, etc.

A particular energy state of a system, such as a hydrogen atom, then corresponds to a particular solution of the Schroedinger equation and to a particular set of quantum numbers. One important property of such a solution, $\psi_i(x, y, z)$, is that $|\psi_i(x, y, z)|^2 \, dx \, dy \, dz$ is proportional to the probability of finding the electron within the element of volume, $dx \, dy \, dz$. The precise circular or elliptical orbits for electrons in the early theories were lost in the elaborate theory in favor of an electron cloud, the density of which gave only the probability of finding the electron.

Quantum mechanics has been so successful in explaining fine

details about hydrogen atoms and many other simple systems that now it is generally believed that it is basically adequate not only to explain complex atoms, but also to predict all of chemistry. In principle, one should be able to predict the whole periodic table and all chemical compounds by calculation. Actually this belief represents a huge extrapolation, because more than 99.9% of the systems of chemical interest are so complicated that, even with high-speed computers, the Schroedinger equation for the system cannot be solved. A two-particle system can be solved exactly but a three-particle system such as H_2^+ or the helium atom already requires approximation methods, and the accuracy rapidly becomes poorer as more particles are considered. It is true, though, that very many important and useful calculations have been made, albeit with approximations, by means of quantum mechanics.

The details of solving the Schroedinger equation for hydrogen atoms are given in many textbooks on quantum mechanics and only some of the results will be noted here. Three quantum numbers, n, l, and m, all restricted to integers, result from the equation, together with the requirement of well-behaved solutions. The total quantum number, n, may be 0, 1, 2, ... and determines the energy of the atom; l may be 0, 1, 2, ..., $(n - 1)$ and indicates the total angular momentum; and m may be $-l$, $-l + 1$, ..., 0, ..., $l - 1$, l and indicates the z-component of angular momentum. Each set of three allowed quantum numbers corresponds to a particular wave function, $\psi_{n,l,m}(r, \theta, \phi)$, the square of which at any point, (r, θ, ϕ), determines density of the probability for locating the electrons.

Often it is desirable to indicate only n and l for an atom and this is done by giving n explicitly and l by using s, p, d, f, g, ... for $l =$ 0, 1, 2, 3, 4, ..., respectively. Thus, e.g., the 3p state for the atom is that for which $n = 3$ and $l = 1$. For s states ($l = 0$) the wave function has spherical symmetry, but for p, d, or f states the electron cloud extends in certain preferred directions.

The main concern here is to see how the theory is extended to many-electron atoms. Addition of even a second electron complicates the problem so much that the Schroedinger equation can be solved only approximately and extension to many electrons in a straightforward manner is quite hopeless. The difficulty arises from the fact that the potential energy of a given electron depends not only on its own coordinates but on those of the other electrons, and these are rapidly moving about, rather than being essentially at rest as the nucleus is.

There is an approximation method, however, that has been used to predict the shell structure of atoms and to explain the periodic variation of chemical properties. This scheme, called the self-consistent-field method, is based on the assumption that the interactions among the electrons can be lumped together so that a given electron moves in the potential field of the nucleus and of another spherically symmetric field caused by the averaged out positions of all the other electrons. This means that the total potential energy of the one electron being considered is a function only of its own distance from the nucleus. Therefore, the Schroedinger equation may be written for one electron at a time and the variables, r, θ, ϕ, are still separable as for a one-electron atom. If $V_i(r)$ (the effective potential energy function in which the i-th electron moves) is known, the Schroedinger equation can be solved, at least by numerical integration methods.

To obtain $V_i(r)$ for each electron in an atom, Hartree (4) used a method of successive approximations. A set of zeroth order wave functions, $\psi_1{}^0$, $\psi_2{}^0$, ..., $\psi_z{}^0$ was assumed, one for each electron, and the average charge density computed for each electron by taking $e|\psi_i{}^0|^2$, where e is the charge of the electron. From the total charge densities of all the other electrons, the potential in which the jth electron moves, $V_j{}^0(r)$, was calculated by the usual methods of electrostatics. This $V_j{}^0(r)$ was substituted in the Schroedinger equation and the solution of this equation gave a new $\psi_j{}^1$. Similarly a whole new set, $\psi_1{}^1$, $\psi_2{}^1$, ..., $\psi_z{}^1$ was obtained. The whole process was then repeated until no further changes occurred in the $\psi_j{}^k$, i.e., until the field was self-consistent. It should be noted that in this approximation each electron was assumed to move in a central force field and therefore the same quantum numbers, n, l, and m, arose as for a one-electron atom. The usual description now used for the electrons in an atom, e.g., of nitrogen in the lowest energy state, two 1s, two 2s, and three 2p electrons, or ($1s^2$, $2s^2$, $2p^3$), is meaningful only in the light of approximations or assumptions such as the above.

Two additional assumptions were needed. The concept of electron spin, with quantum number of plus or minus $\frac{1}{2}$, had already been used to explain details of spectra. The other is the Pauli Exclusion Principle. This says that no two electrons in an atom may have all quantum numbers the same. For $n = 1$ the rules for the quantum numbers require l and m to be zero, and so only two electrons are allowed, with spins of plus and minus $\frac{1}{2}$. For $n = 2$ the allowed (n, l, m) combinations are $(2, 0, 0)$, $(2, 1, 1)$, $(2, 1, 0)$, and $(2, 1, -1)$. Each of these is permitted two electrons with opposite spins for a total of eight in the $n = 2$ shell. It may be noted here that these developments in quantum mechanical descriptions of atoms during the nineteen twenties were partly guided by, and gave most welcome explanations for, empirical information from chemistry. The periodicity in the chemical properties of the elements, first noted by Mendeleeff a half-century earlier, now had a solid theoretical basis. In particular, the closed shells of the noble gases and of many atomic ions included (except for helium) an outer stable group of eight electrons, ns^2np^6. Extensions of the theory to include electronic structures of molecules are more difficult, again because more particles are involved. This topic is discussed in Chapter 10.

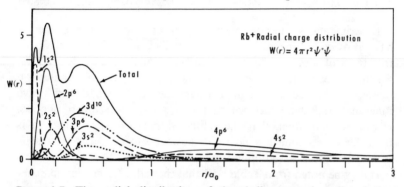

Figure 3.7 The radial distribution of the shells and sub-shells of the Rb^+ ion with a closed shell configuration like that of Kr. Calculated from the self-consistent field approximation. Taken from Leighton, *Prin. of Mod. Phys.*, Mc-Graw-Hill (1959).

Figure 3.7 shows the probability distributions for the various electrons of Rb^+, an ion that is isoelectronic with a neutral krypton atom. The distributions were calculated as functions of radius by the self-consistent-field method. The ordinate is probability per unit radius increment within a spherical shell. Table III.1 gives the radii of maximum radial charge density for the electron wave functions of four of the noble-gas atoms as given by Slater (5, page 210). The figure and table show that for a given atom, it is primarily n that determines the most probable distance of an electron from the nucleus. It should be noted that Fig. 3.7 and Table III.1 give only the radial dependence of the probability, and only the s-electron wave functions have spherical symmetry. For detailed information on the angular dependence of the p, d, and f electron functions, see Leighton (6, Chap. 5) or other textbooks on quantum mechanics.

Table III.1

Radius of Maximum Radial Charge Density as Calculated by
Self-Consistent-Field Methods (Ref. 5, p. 210).
Distances in Ångstroms.

	1s	2s	2p	3s	3p	3d	4s	4p
He	0.30							
Ne	0.055	0.37	0.32					
Ar	0.031	0.19	0.155	0.66	0.67			
Kr	0.015	0.09	0.067	0.25	0.25	0.22	0.74	0.86

Experimental studies by electron, photon and neutron scattering have provided some rather detailed verifications of the radial distributions of electron cloud densities calculated as described above. Furthermore, most theories of chemical binding are also based on these results, especially the angular dependence of the p, d, and f wave functions, and these theories have had a large measure of success. It can be said, then, that the self-consistent-field approximation is basically sound; one has no right, however, to expect exact results from calculations based upon it.

It may be noted from Table III.1 that the radius of maximum probability for a given shell is approximately an inverse function of the nuclear charge. This is consistent with the theorem of electrostatics that for a spherical charge distribution, the field at any radius depends only on the total charge inside that radius and is independent of the charge outside.

Figure 3.7 shows clearly that there is no definite radius to an isolated atom; the charge cloud thins out gradually to smaller probability at larger radii. The one specific number that one might list for the radius of an atom from this theory is the radius corresponding to maximum probability for the outermost shell of electrons. From the curves of Fig. 3.7 it is evident, however, that the electrons spend appreciable fractions of their time at distances greater than that of maximum probability.

Table III.2 lists results, obtained by all of the methods discussed above, for atomic radii of the noble gases. It may be noted with some satisfaction, first, that all the methods yield results of the same order of magnitude and that radii increase with increasing atomic number according to all methods. The values in the first row, based on dielectric constants, may be roughly conceptualized as the distances within which the electrons are very tightly bound to the nucleus. External electric fields can appreciably distort the spherical distributions only beyond these distances. By comparison with the last row it is seen that this tightly bound region extends approximately twice as far out as the probability maximum for the outer shells. Values in rows two and three are nearly alike, as expected, since both depend on distances of closest approach in collisions. The values in the fourth row depend on the distances apart in the solid, where the atoms are nearly at rest. Since these are significantly larger than the closest distances in collisions, we get a picture of flexible spheres that become distorted during collisions like soft rubber balls. The nature of the interatomic forces during collisions is discussed in more detail in the following chapter.

Table III.2

Atomic Radii of the Noble Gases in Ångstrom Units

	He	Ne	Ar	Kr	Xe	Rn
From Eq. (10) and Dielectric Constants of Table II, Chap. II.	0.60	0.73	1.18	1.35	1.59	—
From Eq. (17) and Critical Constants of Table II, Chap. II.	1.13	1.19	1.47	1.58	1.72	1.86
From Eq. (23) and Viscosity Data of Table II, Chap. II.	0.89	1.05	1.48	1.69	1.97	2.24
From X-ray Diffraction Data for the Low Temperature Crystal from Ref. 7.	—	1.57	1.86	2.02	2.19	—
Maximum in Radial Probability from Quantum Mechanics. Ref. 5.	0.30	0.32	0.67	0.86	—	—

The discussion of many-electron atoms thus far has dealt with atoms in their normal, lowest energy, or ground, states. By electron or photon bombardment it is possible for the atomic electrons to be raised to more energetic quantum states. From emission and absorption spectra a vast amount of information has been obtained about excited energy levels. Most of the known energies for the noble gases are those for which one of the outer p electrons has been promoted to a higher energy. Ground states are designated (ns^2, np^6) and a typical excited state is designated $(ns^2, np^5, (n + 1)s)$, where $n = 2, 3, \ldots, 6$

for Ne, Ar, ... , Rn. Since the $(ns^2 np^5)$ part is common to all the known excited states, this may be left out and the typical excited state designated simply as $(n + 1)$s.

Because of electron spins these excited states are multiplets. Space does not permit discussion here of the magnetic interactions of spin with spin, spin with orbital motion and orbital motion with orbital motion between the promoted electron and the core of electrons. Edgell (8) has recently discussed these theories with special application to the noble gases, and the reader is referred to his paper for further references. Suffice it here to give some approximate ranges within which the excited multiplets lie. Table III.3 lists some of these energy values relative to the ground states or to the energy of the normal atom. Instead of listing all levels of a multiplet, of which there may be as many as 12, only the range is given for each set. The table is obtained from detailed tables in Ref. (8), but the units are changed. This brief table, including the ionization energies (complete removal of one p electron), gives quickly some order of magnitude numbers for promotional energies necessary for formation of chemical bonds. By way of comparison, an easily oxidized atom like sodium requires 2.1 electron volts for the first excitation and 5.1 for ionization.

Table III.3

Energy Levels of Noble Gases Relative to the Ground State of Multiplets. Units are Electron Volts.

Atom	Excitation energy	Ionization energy
He	(2s)19.8–20.6, (2p)21.0–21.2, (3s)22.7–22.9, (3p)23.0–23.1	24.59
Ne	(3s)16.6–16.8, (3p)18.4–19.0, (4s)19.7–19.8, (3d)20.0–20.14	21.56
Ar	(4s)11.5–11.8, (4p)12.9–13.5, (3d)13.8–14.3	15.76
Kr	(5s)9.9–10.6, (5p)11.3–12.3, (4d)12.0–13.0	14.00
Xe	(6s)8.3–9.6, (6p)9.6–11.1, (5d)9.9–11.4	12.13
Rn		10.75

24

References

1. L. PAGE and N. I. ADAMS, "Principles of Electricity," D. Van Nostrand, 1958.

2. E. H. KENNARD, "Kinetic Theory of Gases," McGraw-Hill, 1938, page 110.

3. F. W. SEARS, "Thermodynamics, The Kinetic Theory of Gases and Statistical Mechanics," Addison-Wesley, 1953.

4. D. R. HARTREE, *Proc. Cambridge Phil. Soc.* **24,** 89, 111 (1928); Hartree "The Calculation of Atomic Structures," John Wiley and Sons, (1957).

5. J. C. SLATER, "Quantum Theory of Atomic Structure," McGraw-Hill, 1960.

6. R. B. LEIGHTON, "Principles of Modern Physics," McGraw-Hill, 1959.

7. R. W. G. WYCKOFF, "Crystal Structures," Interscience, 1963.

8. W. F. EDGELL, Chap. V of "Argon, Helium and the Rare Gases," G. A. COOK, Ed., Interscience, 1961.

CHAPTER **4**

Pressure-Density-Temperature Relationships and Interatomic Forces

Deviations of gas behavior from ideality were mentioned in the previous chapter in connection with the van der Waals equation. Although these deviations for ordinary pressures and temperatures are quite small for the noble gases, they have been very extensively studied. The reason for this interest is primarily the simple nature of the molecules—they are monatomic and the intermolecular forces between them therefore the easiest to understand. Extensive measurements of pressure-density-temperature relationships for one or more of the noble gases have been made at the Kamerlingh Onnes and the van der Waals laboratories in the Netherlands, at the Physikalisch-Technische Reichsanstalt in Germany, at the University of Durham in England, at the National Research Council in Canada, at the Massachusetts Institute of Technology, and at Harvard. Many of the results of these measurements are listed in a review discussion by Beattie (1).

A common way to present data on gases is to list deviations from the perfect gas law, using one or more terms in a power series in p or in $(1/V)$. Equation (1) is one form commonly used for such an expansion.

$$pV = A + (B/V) + (C/V^2) + \cdots \qquad (1)$$

This is called the virial equation of a gas, and B, C, $\cdots$, which are functions of temperature, are called the second, third, $\cdots$ virial coefficients. Measured data on gases are commonly presented as tables giving A, B, C, etc., as functions of temperature. For high pressures many terms in the expansion may be used, but for ranges not over a few atmospheres the first two terms may be sufficient. An empirical equation, developed by Beattie and Bridgeman (2), gives A, B, C, and D in equation (1) as functions of temperature and this provides a convenient means of tabulating data on virial coefficients. In this equation $A = RT$, $B = RTB_0 - A_0 - Rc/T^2$, $C = - RTB_0b + A_0a - RB_0c/T^2$, and $D = RB_0bc/T^2$. Table IV.1 lists values of the constants for this equation for the noble gases (except radon). As an example, for argon at 300°K these constants give $A = 24.62$ atm-l-mole^{-1}, $B = - 0.38$ atm-l^2-mole^{-2}, $C = 0.028$ atm-l^3-mole^{-3}, and $D = 0$. The Beattie-Bridgeman equation is not precise enough to go beyond the fourth virial coefficient, but when results of measurements are published as tables of virial coefficients, values are commonly given also for the fifth.

Table IV.1

Constants of the Beattie-Bridgeman Equation.
Taken from Ref. (1).

Gas	R $\dfrac{l\,\text{atm}}{\text{deg mole}}$	A_0 $\dfrac{l^2\,\text{atm}}{\text{mole}^2}$	a $\dfrac{l}{\text{mole}}$	B_0 $\dfrac{l}{\text{mole}}$	b $\dfrac{l}{\text{mole}}$	$c \times 10^{-4}$ $\dfrac{l\,\text{deg}^3}{\text{mole}}$
He	0.08206	0.0216	0.05984	0.01400	0	0.0040
Ne	0.08206	0.2125	0.02196	0.02060	0	0.101
Ar	0.08206	1.2907	0.02328	0.03931	0	5.99
Kr	0.08206	2.4230	0.02865	0.05261	0	14.89
Xe	0.08206	4.6715	0.03311	0.07503	0	30.02

To relate measured properties of gases to intermolecular forces, statistical mechanics must be used. The general approach has been to obtain an expression for intermolecular forces from quantum mechanics or from simple models and to use statistical methods to derive expected deviations from the perfect gas law which are then compared to the measured deviations. Fowler and Guggenheim (3) give a good review in their book (Chapter VII) of various methods of calculaton that have been used. The force between two molecules is evidently one of repulsion for small distances and one of attraction for large ones. This has usually been expressed by using two terms for the mutual

27

potential energy function for a pair of molecules. The energy of attraction for two atoms of a noble gas has most often been taken as $-ar^{-6}$, where a is a constant and r the distance between them. The inverse sixth power can be derived from a simple model of the atom that has spherical symmetry in the absence of an electric field but is distorted into a dipole in an electric field. Two such atoms that induce dipole moments in each other will attract each other with a potential given by an inverse sixth power. London derived this form of potential also from quantum-mechanical considerations in 1930.

The force of repulsion was first related to quantum mechanics by Heitler and London in 1927. It is important only at distances where the electron clouds of the two atoms begin to overlap. The general form of the energy of repulsion required by the theory was $R(r) \exp(-r/\rho)$, where $R(r)$ is a polynomial in r and ρ is a constant. Some justification has since been given for simplifying this to just a constant times the exponential for closed shell configurations. This latter approximation has been remarkably successful in correlating the elastic behavior of ionic crystals, where the ions have closed-shell configurations iso-electronic with noble-gas atoms. The range over which r varies is much less, of course, in a crystal than for atoms in the gaseous state. Nevertheless, a relatively simple expression for intermolecular energy that might possibly be valid for all distances is

$$U(r) = P \exp(-r/\rho) - ar^{-6} \tag{2}$$

with three adjustable constants. The first term, a repulsive term, is the important one at small distances and rapidly dies out at larger values of r to leave only the second term, which is attractive. In the statistical calculations it is difficult to relate the first term of equation (2) directly to virial coefficients, and so many workers, following Lennard-Jones (4) have used the form

$$U(r) = br^{-n} - ar^{-6} \tag{3}$$

which is more amenable to computation. Various values have been used for n and fairly satisfactory results have been obtained for values of n ranging from 9 to 14, with some preference given to 12. Equation (3) with $n = 12$ is often referred to as the Lennard-Jones 6–12 potential.

Buckingham (5) used Eq. (2) and tedious numerical calculations to fit the constants to virial coefficients of neon and argon. He could correlate his results also with solid state data and predict the inter-atomic distances in the crystals at 0°K to within 5% and the heats of sublimation to within 2%. His values for the constants in the order neon, argon, were: $P = 25.7$ and 168×10^{-10} ergs; $a = 0.09$ and 1.12×10^{-10} ergÅ^6; and $\rho = 0.235$ and 0.273Å. These constants permit calculations of mutual forces (the force is the derivative of energy with respect to r) and energies of a pair of atoms. Table IV.2 (p. 30) lists calculated values for various distances for both the repulsive and the attractive terms in the forces and also the potential energies. The opposing forces are equal for a net force of zero at 3.12Å separation for neon and at 3.83Å for argon. The calculated closest distances in the crystal at $0°K$ would be less than these values because of attractions of non-nearest neighbors and larger because of zero-point vibrations. Observed values for the crystals are 3.20 and 3.81Å.

Although the net force for neon atoms is zero at 3.12Å, at 20Å the repulsive part has gone down by a factor of 10^{31}, but the attractive part has gone down by a factor of only 10^6. The distances of closest approach in collisions may be estimated by assuming that two atoms, both of average translational energy, are directly approaching each other. At room temperature each will have $(3/2)kT = 62 \times 10^{-15}$ erg and the closest approach will correspond to a mutual potential energy of 124×10^{-15} erg. For neon this gives a closest approach or "collision diameter" of 2.23Å and for argon 3.03Å. These apply, of course, to average translational energies. For the fastest molecules in "head-on" collisions the approaches would correspond to energies several times as large, but since $U(r)$ changes very rapidly in this region, the closest approach distances would be only about ten percent less.

Whalley and Schneider (6) used second virial coefficient data from a wider temperature range than used previously for argon, krypton, and xenon to test three different potential functions. Two were of the form of Equation (3) with $n = 9$ (called the 9:6 potential) and $n = 12$ (called the 12:6 potential) and one was of the form of Eq. (2) (called the exp:6 potential). They found that each of the three forms could be fitted to experimental data so that average deviations between measured and calculated virial coefficients were only two or three times the standard error of the experimental data. The three forms were compared by calculating from each the interatomic distances in the crystals and the heats of sublimation at $0°K$. The results are shown in Table IV.3, which lists percentage errors from measured values.

29

Table IV.2

Mutual Forces and Energies for a Pair of Atoms from Eq. (2) and Buckingham's Constants

	r angstroms	$10^{15}U$ ergs	$10^{13}F_1$ (repulsive) dynes	$10^{13}F_2$ (attractive) dynes	$10^{13}(F_1 + F_2)$ (net) dynes
	2.00	$+377$	$+22.03$	-4.22	$+17.81$
	2.22	$+128$	$+8.64$	-2.03	$+6.61$
	2.23	$+121$	$+8.28$	-1.97	$+6.31$
	2.40	$+47.3$	$+4.02$	-1.18	$+2.84$
	3.00	-5.00	$+0.31$	-0.25	$+0.06$
Neon	3.11	-5.33	$+0.20$	-0.19	$+0.004$
	3.12	-5.35	$+0.19$	-0.19	0.000
	4.00	-2.09	$+0.004$	-0.03	-0.03
	5.00	-0.57	$+6 \times 10^{-5}$	-0.007	-0.007
	10.00	-0.009	$+4 \times 10^{-14}$	-0.0005	-0.0005
	15.00	-0.0008	$+2 \times 10^{-23}$	-3×10^{-6}	-3×10^{-6}
	20.00	-0.0001	$+1 \times 10^{-32}$	-4×10^{-7}	-4×10^{-7}
	2.80	$+387$	$+21.91$	-4.54	$+17.4$
	3.00	$+148$	$+10.54$	-2.86	$+7.74$
	3.03	$+126$	$+9.44$	-2.61	$+6.83$
	3.04	$+119$	$+9.10$	-2.55	$+6.55$
	3.60	-14.8	$+1.17$	-0.78	$+0.39$
Argon	3.82	-18.5	$+0.52$	-0.52	$+0.008$
	3.83	-18.5	$+0.51$	-0.51	-0.0009
	4.00	-17.5	$+0.27$	-0.37	-0.10
	5.00	-6.3	$+0.007$	-0.08	-0.07
	10.00	-0.1	$+8 \times 10^{-3}$	-0.06	-0.06
	15.00	-0.009	$+9 \times 10^{-11}$	-0.004	-0.004
	20.00	-0.002	$+9 \times 10^{-19}$	-0.0004	-0.0004

The 9:6 potential is definitely inferior, but the 12:6 and the exp:6 forms are about equally successful in these predictions.

Abrahamson (7) has recently calculated interatomic potentials for all the noble gases from a detailed quantum-mechanical expression based on the Thomas-Fermi-Dirac statistical model of the atom. His calculations were only for the close range of 0.01Å to 4Å, and

Table IV.3

Percent Error of Calculated Crystal Spacings,
a_0, *and Heats of Sublimation,* ΔH_v

	9:6 Potential		12:6 Potential		Exp:6 Potential	
	a_0	ΔH_v	a_0	ΔH_v	a_0	ΔH_v
Argon	3.0	14.2	1.3	1.7	1.8	6.5
Krypton	3.8	12.4	2.8	4.2	0.8	5.9
Xenon	8.1	17.7	2.8	2.2	1.9	1.9

he compared results with data from molecular beam experiments where the energies were much greater than thermal energies. He found generally good agreement, at least for the smaller distances. He also noted that the 12:6 potential failed badly here but that the exp:6 potential results agreed with experimental results to at least an order of magnitude and often much better at these close distances.

It is interesting to note that all these functions have a minimum of energy and that this may cause atoms of the gas to stick together in dimers. For neon, Table IV.2 shows the depth of this minimum to be (5.35/62) or 8% of the room temperature average molecular energy, and for argon about 30%. For xenon the calculations of Ref. (6) indicate a depth of minimum about 50% of the room temperature molecular energy. In this gas at room temperature or lower there must be an appreciable fraction of atoms moving around in pairs; at suitably low temperatures these pseudo-molecules may survive several collisions.

As the temperature is lowered and pressure is increased, the inter-atomic forces will at some point cause liquefaction or solidification. Equilibria among the phases are indicated qualitatively on *P-T* diagrams in Fig. 4.1. The low temperature phase changes of the noble gases (except for helium) are quite normal. Helium behaves differently than all other gases. Quantum effects are very important for helium and are different for the two isotopes. Figure 4.1(a) is for helium-4. Critical points are known for all the noble gases and triple points for all but helium, and these are given in Chapter 2. For helium, the solid and vapor cannot exist in equilibrium. Instead, there is a strange low-temperature form, called liquid helium II, with unusual properties that include a very low viscosity and very high heat conductivity. A good elementary discussion of the low-temperature behavior of helium is given by Zemansky (8).

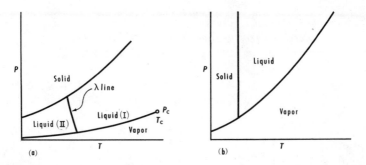

Figure 4.1 Schematic phase diagrams for noble gases: (a) for helium-4; (b) for neon, argon, krypton, or xenon.

The noble gases are, of course, among the most volatile of gases because of the spherical nature of their electron clouds. Table IV.4 gives some selected vapor pressures taken from Hallett's (9) tables.

Table IV.4

Vapor Pressures of the Noble Gases.
Values in Parentheses are for the Solid.

He		Ne		Ar		Kr		Xe	
T, °K	P, mm	T, °K	P, mm	T, °K	P, mm	T, °K	P, mm	T, °K	P, mm
1.0	0.120	16	(1.15)	66	(26)	75	(1.05)	110	(3.0)
2.0	23.77	20	(28.5)	74	(119)	95	(40)	130	(39)
3.0	182.07	24	(250)	80	(305)	115	(490)	160	(560)
4.0	616.54	26	540	90	1003	120	770	170	990
5.0	1478.535	30	1670	100	2440	130	1558	180	1630

References

1. J. A. BEATTIE, Chap. VIII of "Argon, Helium and the Rare Gases," G. A. COOK, Ed., Interscience, 1961.
2. J. A. BEATTIE and P. Bridgeman, *Z. Phys.*, **62,** 95 (1930).
3. R. H. FOWLER and E. A. GUGGENHEIM, "Statistical Thermodynamics," Cambridge Univ. Press, 1949.
4. J. E. LENNARD-JONES, *Proc. Phys. Soc. London*, **43,** 461 (1931).
5. R. A. BUCKINGHAM, *Proc. Roy. Soc. A.*, **168,** 264 (1938).

6. E. WHALLEY and W. G. SCHNEIDER, *J. Chem. Phys.*, **23,** 1644 (1955).
7. A. A. ABRAHAMSON, *Phys. Rev.*, **130,** 693 (1963).
8. M. W. ZEMANSKY, "Heat and Thermodynamics," McGraw-Hill, 1957.
9. A. C. H. HALLETT, Chap. IX of *Argon, Helium and the Rare Gases*, G. A. COOK, Ed., Interscience, 1961.

CHAPTER **5**

Chemical Properties as Known Before 1962

During the seventy years since the discovery of the first of the noble gases, a number of chemists have published accounts of preparations of compounds of one or more of them. These were usually discredited either by the discovery that the observed "compounds" had involved impurities or by the failure of other workers to reproduce the results. During the twenties and early thirties several chemists suggested that the inertness of the rare gases of the atmosphere was a relative matter and that the heavier ones might form compounds. One of these was Linus Pauling, who predicted some of the very xenon compounds that have recently been discovered. His colleagues, Yost and Kaye (1), attempted to prepare xenon fluoride and xenon chloride. Their failure was due to the small amount of available sample of xenon and to the necessity of working in glass apparatus in which formation of SiF_4 probably masked the xenon fluorides that must have been formed. At any rate, their published report of the attempt became a sort of capstone that fixed the legend that the noble gases form no compounds.

Two general lines of evidence for the existence of unstable compounds continued to be of some interest, however. One was the evidence from spectra that diatomic molecules existed in discharge tubes and the other was work on noble-gas hydrates and other clathrates.

Spectra in discharge tubes consist primarily of discrete lines when the source gas is monatomic, but are characterized by bands when the gas consists of diatomic molecules. The bands look like very broad lines that shade off gradually on one side and cut off sharply on the other. At high resolution, the bands may be resolved into numerous regularly spaced lines close together. The main point here is that it is easy to distinguish the spectra of molecules. Now, spectra from discharge tubes containing pure or mixtures of pure noble gases do give evidence for the presence of diatomic molecules by the presence of bands. It is usually not possible to tell, however, whether these are neutral molecules or ions, such as $(Xe_2)^+$ or $(ArKr)^+$. The latter is quite possible because ionization of atoms certainly does take place in the discharge and chemical bond formation seems much more likely when the closed shell arrangement is destroyed by removal of an electron. If neutral molecules do exist, they are probably held together by the weak forces discussed in Chapter 4, and therefore have exceedingly short lifetimes.

Spectroscopic evidence has also been accumulated for the existence of diatomic molecules between noble gas atoms and other atoms. For example, both $(HeH)^+$ and HeH probably exist at least fleetingly. The former is isoelectronic with H_2 and therefore must have energy of stability of the same order of magnitude, but the latter is probably held together by very weak forces. These diatomic species in discharge tubes have not been of great interest to chemists since they are not compounds that can be purified, analyzed, etc., in the traditions of chemistry.

Clathrates are solid mixtures of two kinds of molecules in which one (the host) forms a crystal structure that has cavities large enough to hold the second kind (the guest) of molecules. Of interest here are the combinations in which the guest molecules are noble-gas atoms. For example, hydroquinone forms such a clathrate with argon, krypton, or xenon if it is crystallized out of solution under sufficient pressure of the noble gas. This so-called β crystal modification of hydroquinone does not form at all without some guest atoms being present. In their absence, it solidifies in another crystal form. Apparently the guest atoms are needed to stabilize the open β structure.

Definitions of the word "clathrate" often include the statement that there are no chemical bonds holding the guest atoms or molecules to the host molecules. Since it is difficult to define exactly what is and what is not a chemical bond, it is probably better to compare the energies involved. Very roughly, the energies with which noble gas atoms are bound in clathrates are ten times as high as the van der Waals energies with which two noble-gas atoms are held together as described in Chapter 4. The reason for the greater energies in the

35

clathrates probably lies in the permanent dipoles in the host molecules. On the other hand, the energies in the clathrates are of the order of one-tenth as large as those involved in common chemical bonds.

A review of clathrates in general is given in Ref. (2) and of noble-gas clathrates in Ref. (3). Both include many references to the original work.

References

1. D. M. YOST and A. L. KAYE, *J. Am. Chem. Soc.*, **55**, 3890 (1933).
2. L. MANDELCORN, *Chem. Revs.*, **59**, 827 (1959).
3. G. A. COOK, Chap. VI of "Argon, Helium and the Rare Gases," G. A. COOK, Ed., Interscience, 1961.

CHAPTER **6**

Preparations of Many Compounds, 1962 and After

In 1962, Bartlett's (1) announcement of $XePtF_6$ as a stable compound and the description of XeF_4 as an easily prepared, stable compound by Claassen, Malm and Selig (2) stimulated a widespread research program on the chemistry of xenon and other noble gases. Because the fluorides and oxides of xenon were new, unexpected compounds involving closed electron shells, many chemists and chemical physicists were eager to learn about the properties of the substances and about the nature of the bonds involved. A fortunate result of the excitement among molecular scientists was that many were interested enough to do experiments of their own. Particularly, the national laboratories at Berkeley, Brookhaven, and Oak Ridge, in addition to that at Argonne and the Scientific Laboratory of the Ford Motor Company, were already equipped to handle fluorine routinely and could immediately synthesize the materials so as to make measurements. Several university groups were supplied samples by these laboratories. Research groups in Yugoslavia, Germany, England, and Canada also began experiments immediately. The result was that the most elaborate and sophisticated instrumentation available anywhere for infrared and Raman spectra, x-ray, neutron, and electron diffraction, nuclear magnetic resonance, Mössbauer effect, etc., was used within a few months of the announcement of the discovery of XeF_4 to obtain structural information about the xenon fluorides and oxides.

Most of the results of this early work were reported at a meeting at Argonne National Laboratory in April, 1963. The papers submitted were published in one volume, *Noble-Gas Compounds*, of

400 pages by the University of Chicago Press in October, 1963. This volume was edited by H. H. Hyman of Argonne. Since it contains reports on nearly all of the first year's work in this new field, it will be referred to often.

The noble-gas compounds that have been reported thus far include KrF_2, $KrF_4(?)$, XeF_2, XeF_4, XeF_6, $XeF_8(?)$, $XeOF_4$, XeO_3, XeO_4, $Na_4XeO_6 \cdot X H_2O$ (and other similar salts), various solid compounds of mixed fluorides such as $XeF_2 \cdot 2 SbF_5$, and RnF_x (with x unknown).

6–A XENON FLUORIDES

The fluorides of xenon may be prepared simply by heating the two elements together in a container, preferably made of nickel. To obtain pure compounds it is essential to use a gas-handling system free of oxygen, water, and other materials that easily react with fluorine. Figure 6.1 is a schematic sketch of a typical vacuum line used at Argonne for the preparation and purification of volatile fluorides. The part shown is constructed of nickel and Monel alloys.

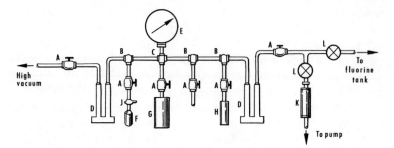

Figure 6.1 Preparation and purification system for volatile fluorides.

It is prepared for use by filling first to an atmosphere with hydrogen and heating all parts but the valves and gage to a red glow so as to reduce the nickel oxides on the inside surfaces. The hydrogen is then pumped out, an atmosphere of fluorine is admitted, and the heating is repeated. This results in a coating of nickel fluoride on the inside that is remarkably immune to further reaction by fluorine or fluorides. In the figure, E is a bourdon gage reading from zero to 1000 mm. Hg that can be read to ±2 mm.; A's are valves with teflon packing; L's are diaphram valves; F is a thin-walled nickel can with a light brass valve, J, that may be removed for weighing of samples; G and H are nickel cans; D's are U-shaped tubes used to condense the materials by cooling with liquid nitrogen or other baths; K is a soda-lime container used to dispose of fluorine. Because of the hazards of possible outward fluorine leaks these lines are always used inside hoods.

A mixture of xenon and fluorine above about 200°C will react and will then consist of a mixture of the elements and the three stable fluorides, XeF_2, XeF_4, and XeF_6, the composition of the equilibrium mixture depending upon temperature and pressure. Qualitatively, for any given temperature, a relatively high fluorine pressure will favor the higher fluoride, etc. The conditions chosen arbitrarily for the first preparation of a xenon fluoride (2) were 400°C with fluorine pressure of 8 atm and xenon pressure of 1.7 atm. These, it has developed, were almost optimum for production of nearly pure XeF_4. At this temperature equilibrium is reached in a reasonable time of the order of an hour, yet the reaction is slow enough to permit cooling to room temperature without changing the concentration much from that at equilibrium at the higher temperature. In the product formed in this way, the XeF_2 and XeF_6 impurities may both be present in the order of one or two percent. Higher purity of XeF_4 may be attained by using somewhat higher fluorine pressures. This increases the XeF_6 impurity and decreases the XeF_2, but the XeF_6 can easily be removed quantitatively after cooling to room temperature. This is possible since the XeF_4 vapor pressure is 3 mm and that of XeF_6 is ten times as much, and the compounds evidently do not form mixed crystals. In a container in which the bulk of the material is solid, the equilibrium vapor will contain mostly XeF_6. If this is rapidly removed several times, the XeF_6 may all be removed while most of the XeF_4 remains.

Pure XeF_2 can be prepared in a nickel container in the form of a tube bent into a vertical loop. If one side is cooled to, say Dry Ice temperature, and the other side is heated, circulation of the mixed gases may carry the XeF_2 molecules out of the hot zone and deposit them on the walls on the cold side before they have time to react with fluorine to produce the higher fluorides. Another method for suppressing the formation of the higher fluorides is heating a mixture of the elements that has a very high excess xenon pressure.

XeF_6 is prepared by heating a 1 to 20 mixture of xenon and fluorine at a pressure of 60 to 100 atm at 300°C for many hours. After removal of excess fluorine the resulting product is over 95% XeF_6. A method of purifying this from the small amount of XeF_4 which is present has recently been described (4). Use of much higher fluorine pressures in the preparation would avoid this purification step, but is practical only for rather small batches.

Xenon fluorides may be synthesized at room temperature or lower if energy is supplied by radiation of some kind or by electric discharge. Mackenzie and Wiswall (3, p. 81) formed a mixture of XeF_2 and XeF_4 at room temperature and pure XeF_2 at $-35°C$ by irradiation of the mixed elements by gamma rays and by energetic electrons. The processes were rather efficient, producing reaction with 5 to 15 atoms of xenon for every 100 electron volts of radiation absorbed.

Weeks and Matheson (3, p. 89) used ultraviolet light of wavelength range 2200–3400Å to form XeF_2 and XeF_4 at room temperature. By circulating the gas through a cold trap to remove the XeF_2 formed, they prepared as much as 8 grams of over 99% XeF_2 in a batch. Yields were as high as one molecule of XeF_2 formed for two quanta of ultraviolet light.

Since elemental fluorine is hazardous but compounds like CF_4 and SiF_4 are simple to handle, the possibility of synthesizing xenon fluorides from these has been investigated by Milligan and Sears (5). They subjected a mixture of xenon and CF_4 at low pressure and low temperature to an electric discharge. They identified XeF_2 among the products thus formed but found no evidence for the higher fluorides. Gard, Dudley and Cady (3, p. 109) heated xenon with CF_3OF at 220°C to 250°C and xenon with FSO_3F at 170° to 180°C. The former yielded XeF_2 and the latter XeF_2 with some XeF_4.

All the techniques used to cause xenon and fluorine to react have in common the probable formation of fluorine atoms. Thus, fluorine gas is slightly dissociated into atoms by thermal energies at temperatures above about 200°C, and ionizing radiations and electric discharges certainly effect some dissociation into atoms. Evidently xenon and fluorine atoms will react at room temperature. Weeks and Matheson (3, p. 94) found evidence, by flash photolysis of a xenon-fluorine mixture, for a diatomic species not found in pure fluorine. They ascribed absorption bands at 3300 and 2500 Å to a transient molecule, XeF. This decayed with a half-life of about 20 microseconds. They suggested the possibility of reactions like $F_2 + h\nu \rightarrow 2\,F$, $F + Xe + F_2 \rightarrow XeF + F_2$ and $XeF + F \rightarrow XeF_2$ for the formation of XeF_2 by ultraviolet irradiation.

In the preparative work with xenon fluorides, analyses were most commonly done by infrared absorption spectra in the range 500 to 650 cm^{-1} (500 cm^{-1} corresponds to $1/\lambda = 500$ cm^{-1}). XeF_2 has

40

its most intense band in this region, a doublet with absorption maxima at 550 and 560 cm^{-1}. In fact, this compound was first established as a stable material by Smith (7) by study of the infrared spectrum. The strongest band of XeF_4 has absorption maxima at 581 and 591 cm^{-1} and XeF_6 has strongest bands at 612 and 520 cm^{-1}. Figure 6.2 shows infrared spectra of samples containing mixtures of the three fluorides.

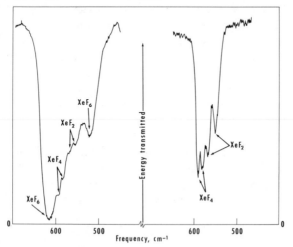

Figure 6.2 Infrared spectra of samples containing two and all three xenon fluorides.

Another valuable tool for compound identification and purity determination is the mass spectrometer. Figure 6.3 shows mass spectra of xenon and of XeF_2 obtained by Studier and Sloth (3, p. 47). Since fluorine is monoisotopic, the isotopic distribution of xenon is repeated for each fragment of a fluoride, in this instance $XeF_2{}^+$, XeF^+, and Xe^+.

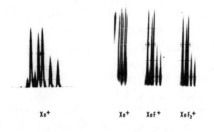

Figure 6.3 Mass spectra of xenon and of XeF_2. From 3, p. 48.

Chemical analyses of fluorides for both xenon and fluorine (Ref. 2) are done most quickly by reduction with hydrogen according to the reaction

$$\text{XeF}_x + \frac{x}{2}\,\text{H}_2 \xrightarrow{\ 300°\text{C}\ } x\,\text{HF} + \text{Xe}$$

Excess hydrogen may be pumped off at $-195°$C and the xenon and HF can be separated easily in a metal vacuum line by trapping the HF at $-160°$C and then the xenon at $-195°$C. The amounts can then be determined by weighing or by other methods. Fluorine analyses have also been done by hydrolysis with NaOH solution and subsequent determination of fluoride by titration with thorium nitrate. Another method has been reaction with mercury to produce Hg_2F_2 and subsequent reaction with NaOH.

Two other xenon fluorides have been discussed. One is a molecular addition compound, of formula $\text{XeF}_2\cdot\text{XeF}_4$ (3, p. 226). This was observed, and its formula determined, by x-ray diffraction of crystals that had formed from mixed XeF_2 and XeF_4 vapors. The other is XeF_8, reported by Slivnik and co-workers (3, p. 64). This was prepared by heating a 16 to 1 fluorine and xenon mixture to 620°C at 250 atm. After cooling to $-78°$C, the excess fluorine was pumped out through a U-tube kept at $-195°$C and the supposed XeF_8 was caught in the U-tube, while the major portion of the xenon was retained at $-78°$C as XeF_6. The XeF_8 was described as pale yellow and said to react rapidly with glass. Further support for the higher fluoride was given by noting that fluoride analyses for XeF_6 samples tended to be high. Efforts at the Argonne National Laboratory to repeat these observations were not successful. Also, quantitative experiments at the Ford Scientific Laboratory on fluorine-xenon equilibria discussed in the next chapter, gave no indication of the existence of a higher fluoride than XeF_6. Most of the evidence cited by Slivnik *et al* for XeF_8 could be explained by assuming some HF impurity in their fluorine. Therefore, the existence of XeF_8 must be considered as highly questionable at this time.

XeF_2, XeF_4 and XeF_6 are all white solids at room temperature with vapor pressures of 3.8, 3, and 29 mm of Hg, respectively. They are usually handled in vacuum, but can be opened to air in a very dry atmosphere. XeF_2 melts at 140°C and XeF_4 at $\sim$114°C.

XeF_6 is a peculiar material that is colorless as a solid, but is bright yellow as a liquid and as a vapor. Its heat capacity has recently been studied by Malm, Schreiner and Osborne (6). Two regions of very high heat capacity corresponding to solid-solid transformations were found in the ranges, -43, to $-3°C$ and $+13$ to $+37°C$. The melting point was observed at $49.22°C$ and a correction calculated so as to predict a melting point of $49.46°C$ for a pure sample. The enthalpy of fusion was found to be 1373 calories per mole.

6–B XENON OXIDE-FLUORIDES, OXIDES, MIXED FLUORIDES, AND CHLORIDE

XeF_6 reacts with silica or with water vapor to produce $XeOF_4$ according to the reactions (3, p. 106)

$$2\,XeF_6 + SiO_2 \to SiF_4 + 2\,XeOF_4$$
$$XeF_6 + H_2O \to 2\,HF + XeOF_4$$

Further reactions, if more water is added are

$$XeOF_4 + H_2O \to 2\,HF + XeO_2F_2$$
$$XeO_2F_2 + H_2O \to 2\,HF + XeO_3$$

The intermediate, XeO_2F_2, has been observed only in the mass spectrometer (3, p. 47) and is probably an unstable compound that cannot be isolated at room temperature. $XeOF_4$, on the other hand, is surprisingly stable. It is nonvolatile at $-78°C$, at which temperature it may be freed of SiF_4 and HF by pumping to a good vacuum. $XeOF_4$ is a colorless liquid with a freezing point of approximately $-30°C$. It can be studied in quartz or glass containers, but reaction with the quartz occurs very slowly with final formation of XeO_3.

XeO_3 is a white crystalline solid that has a small fraction of a millimeter of mercury vapor pressure at room temperature. It cannot be studied at higher temperatures because it frequently detonates even at room temperature. The reaction

$$2\,XeO_3 \to 2\,Xe + 3\,O_2$$

is exothermic, releasing 96 kcal/mole (3, p. 151). It is quite soluble in water and is stabilized by the water, but when the solution is evaporated to dryness at room temperature, the residue is dangerously and unpredictably explosive. Many accidents have occurred with XeO_3 resulting in broken glassware and even nickel containers and some, in injury to workers. Samples larger than one or two milligrams must be handled with great care.

For xenon oxidation numbers lower than six the oxides and oxide-fluorides are less stable, although one might expect two fluorine atoms to be replaceable by an oxygen atom here also. Evidence for the existence of XeO has been found in electric discharges of mixed gases, but no indications have been given that the molecule is stable. $XeOF_2$ has been reported (3, p. 78) to be stable at room temperature, but since the oxygen analysis was done by difference and no further information has been published, this observation must be considered as doubtful. XeO_2 has not been reported. Speculations about heats of formation for some of these are given in the next chapter.

Preparation of XeO_4 has recently been accomplished by Huston, Studier and Sloth (7) by adding sodium perxenate to concentrated sulfuric acid. Their evidence was limited to the mass spectrum and the odor. Selig *et al* (9) characterized the compound further. It is the most volatile compound of xenon known, with vapor pressures of 3 mm at $-35°$, 10 mm at $-16°$ and 25 mm at $0°C$. The solid is unstable and detonates even below $0°C$, but the vapor can be stored at room temperature, at least at low pressure. The infrared spectrum of the vapor is similar to that of OsO_4. The tetroxide was prepared by reaction of either Na_4XeO_6 or Ba_2XeO_6 with concentrated sulfuric acid. The best technique involved the slow addition of the salt to the acid at $-5°C$. At higher temperatures the reaction was so rapid that it caused flashes of fire with decomposition of the product.

A number of adducts of xenon or xenon fluorides with other fluorides have been reported with definite information about their compositions but not including detailed structural work. Bartlett and Jha (3, p. 21) have studied the xenon-platinum hexafluoride adducts. By carefully moderating the reaction by judicious cooling they produced a compound of formula $XePtF_6$. This material did not give an x-ray diffraction pattern nor was magnetic evidence found for the postulated formula, $Xe^+(PtF_6)^-$. The evidence given was indirect and not conclusive. Since xenon in its fluorides and oxides shows a strong preference for even oxidation numbers, a formula, that indicates Xe(I) and Pt(V), must be viewed with skepticism. Other descriptions, such as $XeF_2 \cdot PtF_4$ or $XeF_4 \cdot PtF_2$ should be considered. More rapid reactions between xenon and platinum hexafluoride resulted in a combining ratio of PtF_6/Xe that approached 2. The product of this reaction, upon heating, gave off XeF_4 and left a material of formula $XePt_2F_{10}$. Bartlett and Jha also combined xenon with rhodium hexafluoride with stoichiometry approximating one to one, but did not determine the oxidation state of rhodium in the compound.

Peacock and co-workers (10) reported other covalent compounds of Xe(II) which they described by the formulae: $XeF_2 \cdot 2 \, SbF_5$ and $XeF_2 \cdot 2 \, TaF_5$. Clifford and Zeilenga (10) reported a salt of xenon and gave evidence that it was a compound of Xe(I). This was produced in glass apparatus by means of a high-voltage glow discharge in a two to one mole-ratio mixture of xenon and fluorine at $-78°C$. They formulated it as $(Xe^+)_2 (SiF_6)^{2-}$, but, again the evidence for this is not conclusive. The material was reported to be stable at $-78°C$ but unstable at room temperature. Selig (12) prepared complexes of XeF_6 with BF_3 and with AsF_5. The $XeF_6 \cdot BF_3$ melted at 90°C and had a vapor pressure of less than a millimeter at 20°C. The $XeF_6 \cdot AsF_5$ could not be sublimed under vacuum at room temperature. Peacock, *et al* (13) reported compounds of formulae $XXeF_7$ and Y_2XeF_8 where X may be cesium or rubidium and Y may be cesium, rubidium, potassium, or sodium. The octafluoroxenates of rubidium and cesium were both found to be stable to 400°C.

Gard and Cady (14) prepared an unusually stable complex, $XeF_6 \cdot 2 \, SbF_5$, by adding XeF_6 to SbF_5. This compound melted at 108°C to a clear liquid. They also prepared $SbF_5 \cdot 2 \, XeF_6$ and $XeF_6 \cdot SbF_5$, both of which were less stable.

All the well-characterized compounds of xenon contain xenon bonded only to oxygen or fluorine, but Perlow and Perlow (15) have presented evidence for at least short-time stability of $XeCl_4$ at low temperature. They prepared tracer amounts by transmutation of elements. Iodine-129 decays by beta emission. The resulting xenon-129 nucleus is in an excited state and emits a 40-Kev gamma ray that is suitable for Mössbauer effect studies. Starting with $KICl_4 \cdot H_2O$, in which the ion, $(ICl_4)^-$, is known to have a square-planar shape, they observed the velocity spectrum in the Mössbauer effect of the xenon formed from beta decay of iodine-129. The results indicated covalent bonds in a molecule, $XeCl_4$, of square-planar structure. Since the xenon remains in the excited state for a time of the order of only 10^{-9} seconds, this work says nothing about long-term stability of $XeCl_4$. Furthermore, the experiment was done at 4.2°K, so nothing is known about the possibility of existence of $XeCl_4$ at room temperature.

6–C KRYPTON AND RADON FLUORIDES

After the formation of stable xenon fluorides the obvious question was: "Which of the other noble gases will form fluorides?" The answer, as of now, is "krypton and radon." These elements, however, have not provided as fertile research fields as xenon has.

Krypton will neither react with PtF_6 nor with the even stronger fluorinating agent, RhF_6. Mixtures of krypton and fluorine have been heated to 500°C at high pressures and irradiated by ultra-violet light at moderately low temperatures without evidence of compound formation. Grosse and co-workers (16) first synthesized a krypton fluoride. One volume of krypton and two volumes of fluorine were mixed and subjected to a high voltage discharge at 7 to 12 millimeters of mercury pressure. The walls of the Pyrex container were kept at -188°C. They prepared as much as 1.15 grams of compound in four hours of continuous electric discharge. They found that the material formed colorless crystals, stable at -80°C. They found that at 20°C, 10% of the sample decomposed thermally in one hour, and at 60°C the decomposition was rapid. They observed vapor pressures (of the solid) of 90 mm Hg at 20°C and 28 mm at 0°C. The formula KrF_4 was determined by analysis of the products of thermal decomposition. No other workers have reported preparations of KrF_4, but Hindman, Malm and Schreiner (17) recently prepared krypton fluoride by the same method and repeatedly found the product to be 100% KrF_2. Since this compound has most of the properties reported earlier for KrF_4, it now seems evident that Grosse, *et al* made some mistake in their analyses, and that KrF_4 has not actually been characterized.

Krypton difluoride was first prepared and identified by Turner and Pimentel (3, p. 101) at the very low temperature of 20°K where fluorine and all the noble gases except helium are solid. They deposited a one-to-one mole ratio of Kr and F_2 gases onto a thin layer of solid argon on a CsI window kept at 20°K. This was then irradiated by ultraviolet light for several hours. After the irradiation two infrared bands were observed that were not there before. These were interpreted as the two infrared-active fundamentals of a linear molecule of KrF_2. Verification of the correctness of this interpretation was obtained by MacKenzie (18), who prepared KrF_2 by another method. MacKenzie used a 1.5-Mev electron beam to irradiate an atmosphere of a krypton-fluorine mixture at -150°C (123°K), and thus prepared 100-mg amounts of KrF_2. The material was sublimed at -40°C at a vapor pressure of 1.5 to 2 mm. The formula, KrF_2, was established by decomposing a sample with mercury and analyzing the reaction products. The fluorine was determined by titration and the krypton by gas burette. The krypton was identified by its vapor pressure. KrF_2 is apparently thermodynamically unstable and slowly decomposes spontaneously. The rate is so slow at room temperature, however, that many properties of the compound can be measured.

Since krypton fluoride is unstable but xenon forms a number of stable compounds, one might expect many stable compounds of radon. Unfortunately, in the study of such compounds, one is hampered by the instability of the nucleus; the most stable isotope of radon has a half-life of only 3.8 days.

Work on radon chemistry to date has been limited to the use of very small amounts, of the order of one-fourth millicurie or less (1 curie corresponds to 3.7×10^{10} nuclear disintegrations per second), or to samples of 10^{12} atoms of radon or less. Fields, Stein and Zirin (19) used a nickel vacuum line similar to that shown in Fig. 6.1. In such a line, if 10^{12} atoms were adsorbed to the inside walls uniformly, the average distance between nearest neighbors would be of the order of 500 Å. Even in these small amounts, the radon was found to behave as a gas. It condensed on any part of the line that was cooled to $-195°C$ and then filled the line again upon warming. Locations of the radon were determined by detection of the 1.8-Mev gamma rays emitted by the third daughter, Bi-214. The α and β rays emitted by Rn-222 and the first and second daughters will not penetrate the walls of the vacuum line. The Bi-214 has a 20-minute half-life and its activity grows in slowly where the radon is and then dies out slowly when the radon is moved elsewhere.

Fields, *et al* (19), found that when fluorine gas was added to radon and the mixture was heated, an apparently nonvolatile fluoride was formed. The excess fluorine could be pumped out but the radon fluoride could not, even by prolonged pumping to a good vacuum. The compound could be moved away from one section of the line by heating to 230°C or more, but then it moved only to the nearest cool parts of the line. Radon fluoride was reduced to a volatile form (presumably the elements) by heating with hydrogen gas to 500°C. No information was obtained to indicate the formula of radon fluoride.

Attempts were made to combine radon with chlorine by heating gaseous mixtures to 400 and to 800°C in silica tubes and by irradiating with ultraviolet light for many hours. A mixture of radon and iodine monochloride was heated to 500°C, but in all these experiments the radon, after removal of the halogen, was still in the form of a substance which was volatile at $-78°C$, a good indication that it was elemental radon. When radon and ozone mixtures were subjected to high voltage electric discharge in glass or silica, some of the radon became fixed to the glass so that it could not be removed even by hot 6M nitric acid. This might be interpreted as evidence for the existence of a nonvolatile radon oxide, but similar experiments using oxygen, nitrogen, or helium in place of ozone produced similar results. This suggested that the radon was driven into the glass by ion bombardment, but the possibility of chemical stabilization by formation of oxides or silicates was not ruled out.

An obvious question about the work on radon is: "Why not work with larger amounts, using appropriate shielding for the experimenters?" If one wanted to work with a milligram of radon rather than the millimicrogram amounts of the above experiments, one would need 155 grams of radium as the source from which to pump the radon. If this much radium could be assembled in one place, it, as well as the equilibrium amount of one milligram of radon, would have 155 curies of activity. Shielding of the workers could certainly be accomplished, but the radon compounds themselves could not be shielded and would be subjected to an extremely high level of radiation. As an example, if the supposed milligram of radon were contained in one cubic centimeter, it would be at one-tenth atmosphere pressure. From only the α-radiation (by far the most effective in producing ionization) of radon and its two short-lived daughters, Po-218 and Po-214, there would be ionization energy of 36 electron volts per second per atom. If the average distance the α-particles moved before striking the walls was one-half centimeter and the range in the one-tenth atmosphere radon was 20 cm, one-fortieth of the α energy would be absorbed in the radon. This would be nearly one electron volt per atom per second. With typical chemical bond energies of two or three electron volts, it is clear that stable compounds in the usual sense could not be studied. Thus, an extensive chemistry of radon will probably never be developed, although radon is undoubtedly the least inert of the "inert gases."

6–D POSSIBLE COMPOUNDS OF THE LIGHTER NOBLE GASES

Various workers have made attempts to prepare fluorides or oxides of argon, neon, and helium since hearing of the successes with xenon, but these efforts have not met with success. Generally, it is obvious from the known ionization and promotional energies (see Chapter 3) that compound formation becomes less likely as one proceeds toward the lighter end of the column of noble gases. Nevertheless, there have been serious speculations about possible exceptions. Pimentel and Spratley (20) pointed out that the $(HF_2)^-$ ion, which is common in nonaqueous HF solutions, is isoelectronic with a hypothetical HeF_2 molecule. They made attempts to prepare the latter, but have reported no success. Speculations have also been voiced about the possible existence of argon oxides, even though krypton oxides are unstable. These come from the fact that the oxyacids of chlorine (neighbor of argon) are all common from $HClO$ to $HClO_4$, but for bromine (neighbor of krypton) only one, $HBrO_3$ is common, and many attempts to prepare $HBrO_4$ have failed. Unfortunately, no one knows how to prepare an oxide of any noble gas other than by way of the fluorides, and argon fluorides are almost certainly very unstable.

References

1. N. BARTLETT, *Proc. Chem. Soc.*, 218, (1962).
2. H. H. CLAASSEN, H. SELIG and J. G. MALM, *J. Am. Chem. Soc.*, **84,** 3593 (1962).
3. "Noble-Gas Compounds," H. H. HYMAN, Ed., Univ. of Chicago Press, 1963.
4. I. SHEFT, T. M. SPITTLER and F. H. MARTIN, *Science*, **145,** 701 (1963).
5. D. E. MILLIGAN and D. R. SEARS, *J. Am. Chem. Soc.*, **85,** 823 (1963).
6. J. G. MALM, F. SCHREINER and D. OSBORNE, *Inorg. Nucl. Chem. Letters*, **1,** 97 (1965).
7. D. F. SMITH, *J. Chem. Phys.*, **38,** 270 (1963).
8. J. L. HUSTON, M. H. STUDIER and E. N. SLOTH, *Science*, **143,** 1161 (1964).
9. H. SELIG, H. H. CLAASSEN, C. L. CHERNICK, J. G. MALM and J. L. HUSTON, *Science*, **143,** 1322 (1964).
10. A. J. EDWARDS, J. H. HOLLOWAY and R. D. PEACOCK, *Proc. Chem. Soc.*, **1963,** 275 (1963).
11. A. F. CLIFFORD and G. R. ZEILENGA, *Science*, **143,** 1431 (1964).
12. H. SELIG, *Science*, **144,** 537 (1964).
13. R. D. PEACOCK, H. SELIG and I. SHEFT, *Proc. Chem. Soc.*, 285 (1964).
14. G. L. GARD and G. H. CADY, *Inorg. Chem.*, **3,** 1745 (1964).
15. G. J. PERLOW and M. R. PERLOW, *J. Chem. Phys.*, **41,** 1157 (1964).
16. A. V. GROSSE, A. D. KIRSHENBAUM, A. G. STRENG and L. V. STRENG, *Science*, **139,** 1047 (1963), and Ref. 3, page 75.
17. F. SCHREINER, J. C. HINDMAN and J. G. MALM, *J. Am. Chem. Soc.*, **87,** 25 (1965).
18. D. R. MACKENZIE, *Science*, **141,** 1171 (1963).
19. P. R. FIELDS, L. STEIN and M. H. ZIRIN, *J. Am. Chem. Soc.*, **84,** 4164 (1962).
20. G. C. PIMENTEL and R. D. SPRATLEY, *J. Am. Chem. Soc.*, **84,** 826 (1963).

CHAPTER *7*

Thermochemistry of Xenon and Krypton Compounds

Many questions about the stability of compounds of the noble gases and strengths of the bonds in them are answerable by measurements of thermodynamic quantities. Although such experiments are tedious and time-consuming, a number have already been done, and a consistent picture is beginning to emerge. The heats of several reactions involving xenon compounds have been measured, equilibrium constants in the xenon-fluorine system have been determined, heat capacity work has been started, and heats of sublimation have been evaluated from Clausius-Clapeyron plots. The results of this work, together with comparisons with neighboring elements in the periodic table, make possible some reliable estimates about the stability of compounds not yet prepared.

The Clausius-Clapeyron equation for sublimation may be written

$$\frac{dp}{dT} = \frac{\Delta H_{\text{sub}}}{T(V_{\text{v}} - V_{\text{s}})} \tag{1}$$

If the solid volume, V_{s}, is neglected in comparion to that of the vapor and a perfect gas is assumed this becomes

$$\frac{d(\ln p)}{dT} = \frac{\Delta H_{\text{sub}}}{RT^2} \tag{2}$$

For a temperature interval for which ΔH_{sub} is constant, this can be integrated to give

$$\log p = \frac{-\Delta H}{2.303RT} + \text{constant} \tag{3}$$

A Clausius-Clapeyron plot usually means log p or log f plotted against $1/T$, where f is any property proportional to pressure. The heat of sublimation is then determined from the slope of the line, which is usually straight over fairly large ranges.

Jortner, Wilson and Rice (1, p. 358) determined the heats of sublimation of XeF_2 and XeF_4 using the absorbance of ultraviolet bands for the quantity f proportional to pressure. The vapor in the absorption cell was at room temperature and in equilibrium with the solid phase in a side-arm kept at controlled, lower temperatures. Their plots were straight within experimental error from -15 to $+22°C$. The slopes corresponded to heats of sublimation of 12.3 kcal/mole for XeF_2 and 15.3 for XeF_4. A similar study of XeF_6 was done by the author at Argonne National Laboratory using an absorption band in the infrared at 520 cm^{-1}. He found a value of 14.9 kcal/mole. The vapor pressure of XeF_6 was recently determined accurately by Weinstock, Weaver and Knop (2) over a temperature range of $0°$ to $23°C$. Their data lead to 15.3 kcal/mole for the heat of sublimation.

The most extensive study of thermodynamic properties of xenon fluorides to date has just been completed at the time of this writing by Weinstock, Weaver and Knop. Their results, reported at a meeting of the American Chemical Society (2), were generously made available to the author in a preprint. These workers studied equilibria in the xenon-fluorine system as functions of temperature. Basically their procedure involved keeping a mixture of the elements at a fixed temperature long enough (sometimes up to a week) to reach equilibrium among the various fluorides, xenon, and fluorine. The reaction was then quenched and the elemental fluorine and/or the xenon removed at low temperature and their amounts measured. The total amount of bound fluorine was determined by weight gain. From these data they calculated r, the average number of fluorine atoms bound to a xenon atom in the mixture, and P, the pressure of fluorine in the equilibrium mixture.

r was determined as a function of P for a given temperature of reaction by repeating the experiment with different amounts of reactants. The study included five different temperatures, from 250 to 501°C. Figure 7.1 shows the results of these experiments as plots of r against log P for each temperature. The curves clearly are asymptotic to $r = 6$ at high pressure, indicating that no higher fluoride than XeF_6 was produced in appreciable amounts in the range of conditions studied.

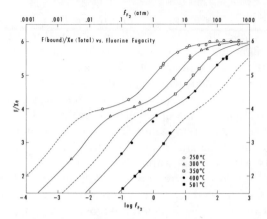

Figure 7.1 Number of bound fluorine atoms per xenon atom as function of fluorine pressure. From Weinstock, Weaver and Knop, Ref. 2.

If only three fluorides exist, three equilibrium constants are sufficient to describe the system. These were defined as

$$\text{Xe} + \text{F}_2 = \text{XeF}_2 \qquad K_2 = \frac{(\text{XeF}_2)}{(\text{Xe})(\text{F}_2)} \tag{4}$$

$$\text{Xe} + 2\,\text{F}_2 = \text{XeF}_4 \qquad K_4 = \frac{(\text{XeF}_4)}{(\text{Xe})(\text{F}_2)^2} \tag{5}$$

$$\text{Xe} + 3\,\text{F}_2 = \text{XeF}_6 \qquad K_6 = \frac{(\text{XeF}_6)}{(\text{Xe})(\text{F}_2)^3} \tag{6}$$

where the parentheses indicate partial pressures. In this notation, with

$$P = (\text{F}_2) \tag{7}$$

$$r = \frac{2(\text{XeF}_2) + 4(\text{XeF}_4) + 6(\text{XeF}_6)}{(\text{Xe}) + (\text{XeF}_2) + (\text{XeF}_4) + (\text{XeF}_6)}$$

Elimination of the partial pressures of the xenon-containing molecules gave the working equation for determination of equilibrium constants

$$r + (r - 2)PK_2 + (r - 4)P^2K_4 + (r - 6)P^3K_6 = 0 \tag{8}$$

Three sets of values of (r, P) for one temperature substituted in this equation gave equations that could be solved for K_2, K_4, and K_6. More than three sets of values permitted internal checking for consistency.

The variation of an equilibrium constant with temperature is related to the enthalpy change or heat of reaction by the van't Hoff equation

$$\frac{d(\ln K)}{dT} = \frac{\Delta H^{\circ}_{\text{reac}}}{RT^2} \tag{9}$$

From this equation the average heats of reaction over the temperature range studied for equations (4), (5), and (6) could be evaluated. These were corrected to lower temperature by means of thermodynamic functions calculated statistically with the aid of known or estimated molecular parameters and vibrational frequencies. The results for the standard heats of reaction were -25.90, -51.51, and -71.25 kcal/mole for XeF_2, XeF_4, and XeF_6, respectively. From these and the literature value of 36.7 kcal/mole for the heat of dissociation of F_2, the average bond energies were determined. For example,

$$\frac{\text{Average bond}}{\text{energy in } XeF_2} = \frac{25.90 + 1(36.7)}{2} = 31.31 \text{ kcal/mole} \tag{10}$$

Similarly, the results were 31.23 and 30.23 kcal/mole for XeF_4 and XeF_6, respectively.

These values of bond energies may be compared with results from calorimetric experiments. Stein and Plurien (1, p. 144) measured directly the heats of the reactions

$$XeF_4 + 2H_2 \rightarrow Xe + 4HF \tag{11}$$

$$XeF_6 + 3H_2 \rightarrow Xe + 6HF \tag{12}$$

The fluoride in each experiment was gaseous and at 120°C. At this temperature both reactions proceeded spontaneously to completion upon addition of the hydrogen. Conditions were such that the temperature rise of the calorimeter was about one degree. Small corrections for the work of addition of hydrogen gas and for change in number of moles of gases present then gave the heat of reaction, ΔH_{reac}. The results are given in Table VII.1.

It is immediately obvious that energy involved in removing a fluorine from the fluoride and attaching it to hydrogen averages (within experimental accuracy) the same for the hexafluoride as for the tetrafluoride. Stein and Plurien used a literature value of -64.2 kcal/mole for the heat of formation of HF and the relation

$$\Delta H_{\text{reac}} = 4\Delta H_{\text{f}}(\text{HF}) - \Delta H_{\text{f}}(XeF_4) \tag{13}$$

$$-202.0 = 4(-64.2) - \Delta H_{\text{f}}(XeF_4)$$

53

Table VII.1

Calorimetric Results of Reduction of XeF$_4$ and XeF$_6$ with H$_2$

	Amount of Fluoride (moles)	Observed Heat (cal)	Correction for *PV* Work (cal)	Calculated ΔH_{reac} (kcal/mole)	Average
XeF$_4$	.00333	−685.8	7.4	−202.2	
	.00157	−325.6	9.9	−199.0	−202.0
	.00159	−337.1	9.5	−204.7	
XeF$_6$	.00201	−626.0	7.8	−305.2	
	.00156	−489.9	9.4	−306.0	−306.5
	.001216	−388.1	10.2	−308.3	

to obtain −54.8 kcal/mole for the heat of formation of gaseous XeF$_4$. Similarly, the heat of formation of gaseous XeF$_6$ was −78.7 kcal/mole. These lead to average bond energies of 32.5 and 31.9 kcal/mole for XeF$_4$ and XeF$_6$, respectively.

Gunn and Williamson (1, p. 133) used completely different reactions to measure similar quantities for XeF$_4$. They added a weighed sample of XeF$_4$ to an H$_2$SO$_4$ solution in a calorimeter and then added solid KI. Most of the xenon was reduced to the element according to the equation

$$\text{XeF}_4 + 2\,\text{H}_2\text{O} \rightarrow \text{Xe} + \text{O}_2 + 4\,\text{HF} \tag{14}$$

but from 5 to 10% remained in solution and was reduced by the iodide according to the equation

$$\text{XeF}_4 + 4\,\text{I}^- \rightarrow 2\,\text{I}_2 + \text{Xe} + 4\,\text{F}^- \tag{15}$$

Since the oxygen and xenon liberated were measured separately by gas burette, the fraction reacting according to Eq. (15) could be calculated, and an overall equation written for each experiment. Using reported values of the heats of formation (aqueous) of H$_2$O, I$^-$, I$_3$$^-$, I$_2$, F$^-$, and HF, they calculated the standard heat of formation of crystalline XeF$_4$ to be −60.1 kcal/mole. If the heat of sublimation from Jortner's experiment, 15.3 kcal/mole, is added to this, the result is −44.9 kcal/mole. This corresponds to 29.6 kcal/mole for the average bond energy of XeF$_4$.

Another different approach was used by Svec and Flesch (3), who studied XeF_2 and XeF_4 with a mass spectrometer and carefully noted appearance potentials (the bombarding electron energy required to produce the ions) for all the ions. From these and suitable assumptions about the ion source reactions, they calculated thermochemical properties. For example, for the assumed reaction

$$XeF_4 \rightarrow Xe^+ + F_2 + F + F^- \qquad (16)$$

they calculated the standard heat of formation by the energy balance

$$AP(Xe^+ \text{ from } XeF_4) = IP(Xe^+) + \Delta H_f(F) + \Delta H_f(F^-) - \Delta H_f(XeF_4)$$
$$12.4 = 12.1 + 0.8 - 2.8 - \Delta H_f(XeF_4)$$
$$\Delta H_f(XeF_4)_{gas} = -2.3 \text{ ev} = -53 \pm 5 \text{ kcal/mole} \qquad (17)$$

Further results, obtained similarly, were $\Delta H_f(XeF_2)_{gas} = -37 \pm 10$ kcal/mole, average bond energy for $XeF_4 = 32 \pm 2$ kcal/mole and average bond energy for $XeF_2 = 39 \pm 10$ kcal/mole.

Johnston, Pilipovich and Sheehan (1, p. 139) measured the heat capacity of solid XeF_4 from 20°K to 300°K. The results for C_p ranged from 1.933 cal/mole deg at 20°K to 28.457 cal/mole deg at 300°. Using the Debye theory with a characteristic temperature of 122°K, they extrapolated the heat capacity to absolute zero and then calculated the standard entropy of the solid at 298.16°

$$S°(XeF_4 \text{ solid}) = 35.0 \pm 1.0 \text{ cal mole}^{-1} \text{ deg}^{-1}$$

For the reaction at 25°C

$$Xe \text{ (gas)} + 2 F_2(\text{gas}) \rightarrow XeF_4 \text{ (solid)} \qquad (18)$$
$$\Delta S°_{reac} = S°(XeF_4) - [S°(Xe) + 2 S°(F_2)] = 35.0 - 137.5$$
$$\Delta S°_{reac} = -102.5 \text{ cal mole}^{-1} \text{ deg}^{-1}$$

Using Gunn's value of -60 for the standard heat of formation, the standard free energy of formation at 25°C

$$\Delta F°_{reac} = \Delta H° - T \Delta S°_{reac} \qquad (19)$$
$$\Delta F°_{reac} = -60 - \frac{298.16(-102.5)}{1000} = -29.4 \text{ kcal/mole}$$

The negative value of this free energy means that xenon and fluorine at one atmosphere will react to form XeF_4 at 25°C provided a suitable catalyst is found.

It is rather clear from measurements made to date that the three well-known fluorides of xenon are thermodynamically stable at room temperature. XeO_3, however, is unstable, and samples have often detonated at room temperature with considerable explosive violence. The heat of formation of XeO_3 was measured by Gunn (1, p. 149) by exploding a small sample of the material in a bomb calorimeter. The sample was introduced into the calorimeter while moist and the water removed by pumping to a good vacuum at room temperature. The sample was then exploded by means of a platinum fuse, the reaction, shown by the equation

$$2\,XeO_3 \rightarrow 2\,Xe + 3\,O_2 \qquad (20)$$

being exothermic. The heat was determined from the temperature rise. Xenon and oxygen were separated by freezing out the former at $-196°C$, and both were measured by gas buret and their purity determined by mass spectrometer. A typical run used 2.763×10^{-4} moles of xenon, produced 1.495 moles of O_2 per mole of Xe and 0.01 mole of CO_2 per mole Xe from some impurity. The heat liberated was 26.67 cal. This was corrected for the CO_2 formed and for the firing energy of the fuse. The average value of $\Delta H_f°(XeO_3)$, after conversion to constant pressure, was $+95.5 \pm 2$ kcal/mole. The positive value makes it quite clear why some of the explosions of XeO_3 are so violent. From this and a literature value of 119 kcal/mole for the dissociation energy of O_2 the bond energy was given as

$$\frac{\text{Average bond}}{\text{energy in } XeO_3} = \frac{-96 - \Delta H_{sub} + 1.5(119)}{3} = 27.5 - \Delta H_{sub}/3 \qquad (21)$$

in kcal/mole. ΔH_{sub} is not known, but it must be large since the molecules are polar.

Gunn (4) recently measured the heat of explosive decomposition of XeO_4 gas to its constituent elements in a calorimeter. After correcting for pV work, he obtained $+153.5$ kcal/mole for $\Delta H_f°$ (XeO_4, g). This gave for the bond in XeO_4

$$\frac{\text{Average bond}}{\text{energy in } XeO_4} = \frac{-153.5 + 2(119)}{4} = 21.1,$$

in kcal/mole.

Thus the energy of the Xe-O bond is significantly less than the 31 kcal/mole found for the Xe-F bond.

A summary of the discussed heats of formation and bond energies of the xenon fluorides is given in Table VII.2.

Table VII.2

Heats of Formation and Bond Energies (*kcal/mole*)

Observers	Weinstock, Weaver and Knop	Stein and Plurien	Gunn and Williamson	Svec and Flesch
XeF$_2$ ΔH_f(gas)	−25.90			−37
Aver Bond E	31.3			39
XeF$_4$ ΔH_f(gas)	−51.51	−54.8	−44.9*	−53
Aver Bond E	31.23	32.5	29.6*	32
XeF$_6$ ΔH_f(gas)	−71.25	−78.7		
Aver Bond E	30.23	31.9		

*assumes 15.3 kcal/mole for ΔH_{sub} (XeF$_4$)

Although there is some spread among the values, the average bond energy is clearly near 30 kcal/mole for all three fluorides. That the bond energy is nearly the same within experimental error is surprising and it certainly argues for similar bonding orbitals in all the fluorides.

If the assumption is made that similarly, the bond energy for Xe-O is independent of the remainder of the molecule, and that this independence holds, even for mixed oxide-fluorides, predictions may be made about probable stability of various compounds not yet studied. The energy balance for the reaction, represented by the equation

$$\text{Xe} + \frac{x}{2}\,\text{F}_2 + \frac{y}{2}\,\text{O}_2 \rightarrow \text{XeO}_y\text{F}_x \qquad \textbf{(22)}$$

then requires that

$$\Delta H_f(\text{XeF}_x\text{O}_y) = -\frac{x}{2}\,\Delta H_f(\text{F}_2) - \frac{y}{2}\,\Delta H_f(\text{O}_2) - x(\text{B.E. of Xe-F})$$

$$- y(\text{B.E. of Xe-O}) \qquad \textbf{(23)}$$

Substitution of the known quantities on the right side yields

$$\Delta H_f(\text{XeF}_x\text{O}_y) = -\frac{x}{2}\,(-36.7) - \frac{y}{2}\,(-119) - x(30) - y(21.1)$$

$$= -11.7x + 38.4y \qquad \textbf{(24)}$$

in kcal/mole. This equation yields heats of formation for xenon oxide-fluorides for which measurements are not available as shown in Table VII.3. These predictions, of course, are highly speculative, but

Table VII.3

Rough Predicted Values from Equation (24)
of Heats of Formation from the Elements

Compound	Heat of Formation (kcal/mole)
XeF_8	-94
XeO	$+38$
XeO_2	$+77$
$XeOF_2$	$+15$
$XeOF_4$	-9
XeO_2F_2	$+53$
$XeOF_6$	-32
XeO_2F_4	$+29$
XeO_3F_2	$+92$

they indicate only two mixed oxide-fluorides with thermodynamic stability. $XeOF_4$ is, in fact, the only one that has been chemically isolated and characterized. The indications that XeF_8 and $XeOF_6$ are stable are probably quite incorrect because steric hindrance would prevent bonds to more than six atoms around the xenon atom. Since even XeO_4, the most unstable of all, has been prepared and studied, it is quite likely that other mixed oxide-fluorides will be characterized, but they will probably not be thermodynamically stable.

Predictions about the stability of xenon and krypton compounds based on comparisons with elements to the left of the noble gases in the periodic table were made recently by Bartlett (4). Average bond energies of the fluorides are shown as functions of atomic number in Fig. 7.2. For the series SbF_3, TeF_4, IF_5, and XeF_6, all points were known and lay on a smooth curve. The higher fluorides, SbF_5, TeF_6, and IF_7 were then used to predict a stable XeF_8. Again, the difficulty of crowding eight fluorine atoms around one xenon atom may destroy the validity of this prediction. Similarly, bond energies for AsF_3, SeF_4, $BrF_5(BrF_3)$ and the observed instability of KrF_4 fit into a consistent pattern. The higher bond energy of BrF was taken as suggestive that KrF_2 may be stable. Similarly Fig. 7.3 shows rather clearly that oxides and chlorides of xenon will be unstable compounds.

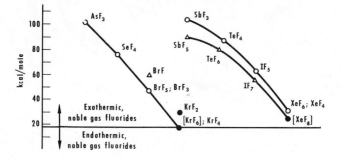

Figure 7.2 Average bond energy (kcal/mole for some fluorides. Square brackets indicate unknown compounds, open circles, experimental values. From Bartlett, Ref. 4.

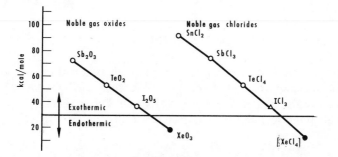

Figure 7.3 Average bond energies (kcal/mole) for some oxides and chlorides. Square brackets indicate unknown compounds; open circles, experimental values; closed circles, theoretical values. From Bartlett, Ref. 4.

References

1. "Noble-Gas Compounds," H. H. HYMAN, Ed., Univ. of Chicago Press, 1963.
2. B. WEINSTOCK, E. E. WEAVER and C. P. KNOP, *Div. of Inorg. Chem. of Am. Chem. Soc. Abstracts of Papers at 148th Meeting,* Chicago, Aug. 31—Sept. 4, 1964.
3. H. J. SVEC and G. D. FLESCH, *Science,* **142,** 954 (1963).
4. N. BARTLETT, *Endeavour,* **23,** 3 (1964).

CHAPTER **8**

Solution Chemistry

8–A ANHYDROUS HYDROGEN FLUORIDE SOLUTIONS

When xenon fluorides first became available, hydrogen fluoride seemed a natural solvent for studies of them in solution. These studies were undertaken by Hyman and Quarterman (8, p. 275). Their solubility data are reproduced as Table VIII.1.

Table VIII.1

Solubility of Xenon Fluorides in Anhydrous HF

Compound	Temperature (degrees C)	Solubility (moles/1000 gm)
XeF$_2$	− 2.0	6.38
	+12.25	7.82
	29.95	9.88
XeF$_4$	20	0.18
	27	0.26
	40	0.44
	60	0.73
XeF$_6$	15.8	3.16
	21.7	6.06
	28.5	11.2
	30.25	19.45

The solubilities were determined by preparing the mixtures in transparent polychlorotrifluoroethylene (Kel-F) tubes and observing repeatedly the temperatures at which the last crystals of solute disappeared in the liquid HF. The data fit straight lines reasonably well in plots of logarithm of solubility against reciprocal temperatures. From the slopes of these lines the heats of solution were estimated as 2.5, 6.7, and 18 kcal/mole for XeF_2, XeF_4, and XeF_6, respectively.

Although XeF_2 is more soluble than XeF_4 by a factor of 25, the two solutions were similarly clear and colorless and no electrical conductivity could be detected. Various observations indicated solution without reaction, ionization, or unusual interaction. XeF_4 behaved as an active fluorinating agent in solution. Benzene was attacked rapidly and metals like platinum and molybdenum were slowly converted to fluorides.

The hexafluoride, on the other hand, was found to be ionized in solution. The molar conductivity for 0.02 mole/liter, the most dilute sample studied, was 150 cm^2/ohm at 0°C, corresponding to a degree of ionization possibly as high as 50%. Although no definite information on mode of ionization was obtained, a reasonable guess would include $(XeF_5)^+$ and $(HF_2)^-$ ions. The solutions of XeF_6 were very active chemically. Kel-F tubes had always been completely adequate to handle HF solutions, but the XeF_6 solutions repeatedly produced cracks in the tubes and sometimes caused a complete break.

8–B HYDROLYSIS REACTIONS

Publication of the first paper on xenon tetrafluoride was held up a week or longer because of puzzling analytical results. The method of analysis involved hydrolysis in water. It was expected that the xenon would be immediately reduced to the element according to: $XeF_4 + 2 H_2O \rightarrow Xe + O_2 + 4 HF$. The amount of fluoride in the water was as expected, but the amounts of xenon and oxygen that could be pumped off were much too low. The immediate analytical problem was solved by using hydrogen instead of water to reduce the xenon, but the early suspicions that stable aqueous xenon complexes may exist has been developed to an extensive solution chemistry of xenon.

Important contributions to the unraveling of the solution chemistry were made by Williamson, Koch, and co-workers (8, pp. 158, 181) (1) of the University of California; by Dudley, Gard and Cady (2) of the University of Washington; by Kirschenbaum and Grosse (3) of Temple University; and by Malm, Appelman and others (8, pp. 167, 185) at Argonne. A general discussion of the work at Argonne with references to the other work has recently been written by Appelman and Malm (4) (5) and generously made available to the author before publication. For further details these papers should be consulted.

All three fluorides of xenon react with water, the vigor of the reaction increasing with number of fluorine atoms per molecule. If XeF_2 crystals are added to pure water at 0°C they slowly dissolve until saturation is reached at around 25 mg per ml of water. A very slow rate of bubble formation is observed also, as well as a pungent odor. The gas coming off as bubbles is primarily a mixture of Xe and O_2 in a two to one molar ratio. The component responsible for the odor is probably a small amount of XeF_2 vapor.

The solution of XeF_2 is strongly oxidizing. It rapidly oxidizes HCl to chlorine, iodate to periodate, and Ag(I) to Ag(II). It slowly reacts with water releasing xenon and oxygen as noted above. At 0°C this reaction is so slow as to release only half the xenon in seven hours, but the rate is many times as great at room temperature. If the solution is made alkaline or if excess thorium ion is added, the xenon is all released within a few minutes. Good evidence has been given that the Xe(II) in solution is undissociated XeF_2 and that the reaction of decomposition is

$$XeF_2 + H_2O \rightarrow Xe + \tfrac{1}{2} O_2 + 2\,HF \tag{1}$$

or

$$XeF_2 + 2\,(OH)^- \rightarrow Xe + \tfrac{1}{2} O_2 + 2\,F^- + H_2O \tag{2}$$

Appelman and Malm found that immediately after the XeF_2 dissolved, very little F^- was present as indicated by potentiometric titration with base, but that the concentration of F^- gradually increased with time. They also used an ultraviolet absorption band at 243 millimicrons to establish the presence of XeF_2 molecules in solution and to verify that their concentration accounted for all that was dissolved. This band was shifted from 230 millimicrons for the vapor to 243 for the solution and was slightly broadened, but otherwise the two bands were very similar in appearance.

No definite evidence for Xe(II) in any other form than XeF_2 has been obtained but Appelman and Malm offered the speculation that a transient bright yellow color seen when XeF_2 solutions are made basic may be due to an unstable XeO.

The early experiments on hydrolysis of XeF_4 alluded to above were repeated and extended at several laboratories. This work finally established an overall stoichiometry given by

$$3\,XeF_4 + 6\,H_2O \rightarrow XeO_3 + 2\,Xe + 1.5\,O_2 + 12\,HF \qquad (3)$$

In these experiments a common procedure was to condense a weighted amount of the XeF_4 vapor into a glass bulb at liquid nitrogen temperature and then to add water slowly in a carefully evacuated system so that it froze in the bulb. The reaction, with evolution of xenon and oxygen, took place slowly, as the mixture warmed to room temperature. The two gases were sometimes pumped into a bulb of known volume by means of a Toepler pump, their total determined by pressure and temperature measurement, and the ratio obtained by mass spectrometer. In other experiments the evolved gas mixture was separated by trapping the xenon in a glass U-tube at $-195°C$ as the oxygen was pumped through. The fluoride was determined by titration. The oxidizing power of the xenon left in solution served to identify it as $Xe(VI)$. Evidence for the formula, XeO_3 is discussed below.

Disproportionation of $Xe(IV)$ into $Xe(VI)$ and $Xe(O)$ according to Equation (3) occurs in pure water, dilute acid, or dilute base. A plausible mechanism to explain this stoichiometry has been given (4) as

$$3\,XeF_4 + 6\,H_2O \rightarrow 2\,XeO + XeO_4 + 12\,HF \qquad (4)$$

$$2\,XeO \rightarrow 2\,Xe + O_2 \qquad (5)$$

$$XeO_4 \rightarrow XeO_3 + 0.5\,O_2 \qquad (6)$$

No evidence has been found for any $Xe(IV)$ that is stable even for a short time in water. A transient yellow color was seen in many of the experiments of hydrolysis of XeF_4. Again, this may be associated with the XeO of Eqs. (4) and (5).

For XeF_2 all the xenon is reduced by water and for XeF_4 two-thirds of it is reduced to the element, but in the case of XeF_6, as Dudley, *et al.* first pointed out (2), all the xenon may be retained in solution as $Xe(VI)$. The reaction is simply

$$XeF_6 + 3\,H_2O \rightarrow XeO_3 + 6\,HF \qquad (7)$$

and may be carried out with pure water, dilute acid, or dilute base.

63

8-C XENON OXY-ACIDS AND THEIR SALTS

Very pure Xe(VI) solutions were prepared (4) by hydrolysis of XeF_6 at low temperature in the presence of enough MgO to neutralize rapidly all the HF produced. The excess MgO was filtered out and the magnesium removed from the solution by means of a column of hydrous zirconium phosphate that had been washed with perchloric acid. Residual fluoride was then removed by a column of hydrous zirconium oxide that had been converted to the nitrate form by washing with dilute nitric acid. The resulting "xenic acid" was entirely stable and could be concentrated to approximately four molar before crystallization began. The anhydride deposited upon evaporation to dryness was clearly the unstable XeO_3 that could be detonated by slight warming or by mechanical shock, but this decomposition was not initiated before the crystals appeared dry.

Xenic acid is a very weak acid. Conductance measurements indicate that it is a nonelectrolyte. A solution $0.8M$ in Xe(VI) and $0.04M$ in $(ClO_4)^-$ has a net molal freezing point depression of 1.95 ± 0.15 degrees, an indication of only one xenon atom per molecule or ion. The Raman spectrum of the solution is discussed in the next chapter, but it indicates that the primary molecular species in a $2M$ solution is XeO_3 molecules. No odor has been detected in vapors from these solutions. Dilute solutions were concentrated by a factor of ten without loss of xenon by vacuum distillation at room temperature. Less than 0.01% of the xenon appeared in the distillate (4).

Although the primary molecular constitution of concentrated xenic acid is undoubtedly undissociated XeO_3, there is ample evidence that some reaction with water occurs, especially at high pH. Williamson and Koch (1) established this first by dissolving solid XeO_3 in water enriched with O^{18}. After some time the water was removed by evaporation and the XeO_3 residue analyzed for O^{18} content. Nearly complete exchange had occurred in an hour. This experiment established that some equilibrium reaction was present, but did not detail it.

Appelman and Malm (4) found that the ultraviolet spectra of $0.003M$ solutions of Xe(VI) are nearly independent of pH below pH 10 and above pH 11, but change between 10 and 11. They titrated solutions $0.07M$ in Xe(VI) and $0.5M$ in $NaClO_4$ with $0.5M$ NaOH. The titration curve showed a slight inflection at $OH^-/Xe = 1$, and so they analyzed the curve with the assumption that the equilibrium was

$$(HXeO_4)^- \rightleftarrows XeO_3 + (OH)^- \qquad (8)$$

The equilibrium constant calculated for this reaction is 6.7×10^{-4}, and no evidence was found for any further deprotonation. Thus the $(HXeO_4)^-$ ion is present in appreciable amount only when the $(OH)^-$ concentration is high, and no definite evidence is available for other ionic species.

Xenic acid is a moderately strong oxidizing agent. Iodide is rapidly oxidized in acid solution and slowly above pH 7. Chloride is oxidized to chlorine slowly in $2M$ HCl and very rapidly in $6M$ HCl. In $6M$ perchloric acid bromine is slowly oxidized to bromate. In all these reactions the xenon is reduced to the element.

Salts of xenic acid (H_2XeO_4) are named xenates and salts of H_4XeO_6 (perxenic acid) are perxenates. Whether stable xenates exist has been the subject of some discussion, but very recently alkali xenates have been characterized. Kirschenbaum and Grosse reported that a salt precipitated from xenic acid by addition of barium hydroxide was stable up to 125°C and was analyzed as Ba_3XeO_6. They also reported that solutions of sodium and potassium salts of Xe(VI) were stable. Malm and Appelman, however, more recently (4) found that barium xenate disproportionated rapidly at room temperature with evolution of xenon and oxygen. After 15 minutes, only 49.6% of the xenon was left and 65.7% of the original oxidizing power. They suggested a set of reactions to account for these observations

$$2\,XeO_3 + 2\,Ba(OH)_2 \xrightarrow{fast} 2\,BaXeO_4 + 2\,H_2O \qquad (9)$$

$$2\,BaXeO_4 \xrightarrow{moderate} Ba_2XeO_6 + XeO_2 \qquad (10)$$

$$XeO_2 \xrightarrow{fast} Xe + O_2 \qquad (11)$$

the conversion to barium perxenate being complete after 15 minutes at room temperature. After vacuum drying, the precipitate was analyzed as $Ba_2XeO_6 \cdot 1.5\,H_2O \cdot 0.05\,BaCO_3$. The barium perxenate was found to be stable up to approximately 300°C.

Spittler and Jaselskis (6) prepared mono sodium, potassium, cesium, and rubidium xenates. They mixed equal volumes of $0.01M$ aqueous XeO_3 and $0.01M$ alkali hydroxide and quickly froze the solution in liquid nitrogen. The water was then pumped away by means of a vacuum pump as the sample slowly warmed to room temperature. The remaining powdered material was established as a

65

single compound, rather than a mixture of XeO_3 and alkali hydroxide crystals, by infrared spectroscopy and by x-ray diffraction. Sodium xenate is apparently stable when stored in a vacuum, but it decomposes explosively when heated above approximately 160°C. The salt is soluble in water, but immediately begins to decompose in aqueous solution.

When XeF_6 is added to concentrated sodium hydroxide the Xe(VI) slowly disproportionates to Xe(O) and Xe(VIII). The sodium salt of the latter is only slightly soluble, and at room temperature it precipitates over a period of many hours while xenon and oxygen gases are given off. This reaction was studied by Appelman and Malm by making periodic determinations of concentrations of Xe(VI) and of Xe(VIII) as the reaction proceeded to completion. Results from a typical experiment are outlined in Table VIII.2. The value of approximately 4 for the ratio of lost oxidizing power to lost xenon, was taken to imply the reaction

$$2\,XeF_6 + 4\,Na^+ + 16\,(OH)^- \rightarrow$$
$$Na_4XeO_6 + Xe + O_2 + 12\,F^- + 8\,H_2O \qquad (12)$$

Williamson and Koch (7) studied a similar reaction by adding sodium hydroxide to a pure XeO_3 solution. They found the rate of reaction to be independent of $(OH)^-$ concentration and the Xe and O_2 to be given off in a one-to-one mole ratio. They postulated an intermediate of Xe(IV) according to

$$2\,XeO_3 + 2\,H_2O \xrightarrow{\text{slow}} XeO_2 + H_4XeO_6 \qquad (13)$$

$$H_4XeO_6 + 4\,NaOH \xrightarrow{\text{fast}} Na_4XeO_6 + 4\,H_2O \qquad (14)$$

$$XeO_2 \xrightarrow{\text{fast}} Xe + O_2 \qquad (15)$$

$$2\,XeO_3 + 4\,NaOH \rightarrow Na_4XeO_6 + Xe + O_2 + 2\,H_2O \qquad (16)$$

The sodium perxenate produced according to equation (12) tends to be contaminated by NaF which also is only slightly soluble. The method of Eq. (16) is wasteful of xenic acid, but nearly all the xenon can be retained by bubbling ozone through a solution of XeO_3 in molar NaOH (4). The xenon is oxidized to Xe(VIII) and sodium perxenate is precipitated nearly quantitatively before the reaction represented by Eqs. (13) and (15) wastes much xenon. Since the perxenate is only slightly soluble it may be washed to remove hy-

Table VIII.2

Disproportionation of XeF$_6$ in 2.5M NaOH

Time (hrs)	Xe(VI) (millimoles)	Xe(VIII) (millimoles)	Lost Oxidizing Power / Lost Xenon
0	1.392	—	—
2	0.699	0.337	4.11
6	0.187	0.628	3.82
11	0.037	0.692	3.91
23	—	0.704	3.95

droxide. Appelman and Malm found the product prepared this way to be pure except for two mole percent sodium carbonate. After the precipitate was dried it was analyzed as $Na_4XeO_6 \cdot 2\,H_2O$. Crystalline phases of this material have also beeen prepared with six or eight water molecules. All water of hydration can be removed at around 100°C.

All three methods described for the preparation of sodium per-xenate were tried with potassium in place of sodium (4), but the solid product could hardly be dried without explosion. The unstable solid was found to be $K_4XeO_6 \cdot 2\,XeO_3$. Koch and Williamson (7) prepared $K_4XeO_6 \cdot 9\,H_2O$, and found crystals of this material to be stable enough for single crystal x-ray diffraction studies. Perxenates of silver, lead, and uranium were prepared by Gruen (8, p. 174) by allowing solid sodium perxenate to react with aqueous solutions of silver nitrate, lead nitrate, and uranyl nitrate. In each case he found the solid salt to be stable to around 150°C.

Although crystalline sodium perxenate is so stable that it can be heated to nearly 300°C without decomposition, aqueous solutions are unstable. A $0.003M$ solution has a pH of 11.5 and has been found to decompose at room temperature at a rate of about 1% per hour (4). At pH 8 the rate was over 1% per minute and below pH 7 the decomposition was almost instantaneous. In these reactions oxygen was released and the Xe(VIII) was reduced to Xe(VI).

Since only Xe(VI) is stable in acid solutions, routine determinations of xenon concentrations (4) were done by first adding acid to convert any Xe(VIII) to Xe(VI), adding excess sodium iodide, and titrating the triiodide formed with standard thiosulfate to an amylose end-point. On the other hand, if the iodide was added before acidifying, the total oxidizing power was indicated in the titration. The ratio of this latter titer to the former, multiplied by six, gave the mean oxidation number of the xenon. For aliquots from freshly dissolved sodium perxenate this ratio of titers was always 4/3, but as decomposition progressed it approached unity.

Xe(VIII) solutions are unusually powerful oxidizing agents. They oxidize iodide to iodine rapidly even in molar base solutions and chloride to chlorine in dilute acid. They convert Mn^{2+} immediately to permanganate in dilute acid. The latter two reactions occur so rapidly that they compete favorably with the release of oxygen, which also occurs rapidly in acid solution (4).

The nature of ionic and molecular species in Xe(VIII) solutions has been studied by Appelman and Malm by means of ultraviolet absorption spectra and potentiometric titrations. From the variation of the spectra as functions of pH (fixed by buffers) the conclusion was drawn that between pH's of 7.5 and 13 there were only two important species contributing to the absorption. Change of concentration from 3×10^{-4} to $3 \times 10^{-3} M$ did not appreciably affect the spectrum provided that concentration times length of absorbing path was held constant. This indicated that the equilibrium did not involve a change of aggregation of molecules.

Titration of sodium perxenate with acid was used to obtain clues about the nature of the equilibria and the ionic species involved in the reduction of Xe(VIII) to Xe(VI) that occurs rapidly upon acidification. Because of the ease of decomposition, the titrations were done as rapidly as possible, but decomposition introduced considerable uncertainty as the solution became acidic. Figure 8.1 is the titration curve taken from Ref. (4). The initial pH in newly-prepared solutions of sodium perxenate corresponds approximately to the liberation of one $(OH)^-$ per molecule dissolved, and this was taken to suggest the reaction

$$Na_4XeO_6 + H_2O \rightarrow (HXeO_6)^{-3} + (OH)^- + 4\,Na^+ \qquad (17)$$

Figure 8.1 shows that upon the addition of more than two moles of acid per mole of xenon, the pH began to drop rapidly with further acid. A tendency for rapid recovery of the high pH was noted, however, until four moles of acid had been added per mole of xenon, after which the pH rose steadily. The conclusion was that after H^+/Xe reached two, a decomposition reaction consumed another two moles of acid per mole of xenon.

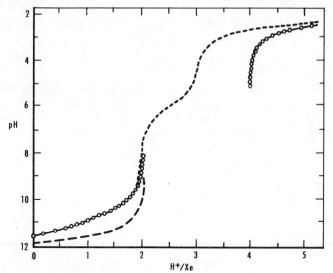

Figure 8.1 Titration of $0.003M$ perxenate with $0.1M$ HClO$_4$ at 24°C. Solid line with circles is actual titration, dotted line is calculated curve assuming no decomposition, dashed line is reference curve for titration of (OH)$^-$. Taken from Ref. (4).

The slight flattening of the solid curve around H$^+$/Xe = 1.5 was taken as evidence for protonation of a weak base by the second mole of acid, the first mole having neutralized the (OH)$^-$ produced as shown in Eq. (17). Finally, after complete conversion to Xe(VI), addition of acid produces no further chemical change. The set of reactions postulated to explain the titration curve was

$$(HXeO_6)^{-3} + H^+ \rightleftarrows (H_2XeO_6)^{-2} \tag{18}$$

$$(H_2XeO_6)^{-2} + H^+ \rightleftarrows (H_3XeO_6)^- \tag{19}$$

$$(H_3XeO_6)^- \rightarrow (HXeO_4)^- + 0.5\,O_2 + H_2O \tag{20}$$

$$(HXeO_4)^- \rightleftarrows XeO_3 + H_2O \tag{21}$$

From Eqs. (18) and (19), the hypothetical reaction

$$(H_3XeO_6)^- + H^+ \rightleftarrows H_4XeO_6 \tag{22}$$

and estimated equilibrium constants, the dashed titration curve below pH 8 was calculated for the hypothetical case of no decomposition.

69

Equation (18) was considered to be the main reaction occurring at high pH and the two main species contributing to the spectra referred to above were thought to be $(HXeO_6)^{3-}$, predominant at pH 13, and $(H_2XeO_6)^{2-}$, predominant at pH 7.5.

Rough estimates for oxidation potentials were also deduced from this work. In acid solution, the $Xe - Xe(VI)$ potential must be in the neighborhood of 1.8 volts and that of $Xe(VI) - Xe(VIII)$ about 3 volts. In basic solution, both were set at about 0.9 volts.

Aqueous xenic acid, as noted above, is quite stable and may be evaporated to give the solid anhydride, XeO_3, but salts are difficult to prepare. Aqueous perxenic acid, on the other hand, is unstable, as shown in Eqs. (20) and (22) above, but salts such as sodium perxenate are surprisingly stable. Recently the anhydride of perxenic acid, XeO_4, has been prepared from sodium and barium perxenates as described in Chapter 6. The formula was established by mass spectrometer, by analysis of the gaseous products of decomposition, and by comparison of its infrared spectrum with those of $(IO_4)^-$ and OsO_4 (Refs. (7) and (8) in Chap. 6).

References

1. S. M. WILLIAMSON and C. W. KOCH, *Science*, **139**, 1046 (1963). D. H. TEMPLETON, A. ZALKIN, J. D. FORRESTER and S. M. WILLIAMSON, *J. Am. Chem. Soc.*, **85**, 817 (1963).

2. F. B. DUDLEY, G. GARD and G. H. CADY, *Inorg. Chem.*, **2**, 228 (1963).

3. A. D. KIRSCHENBAUM and A. V. GROSSE, *Science*, **142**, 580 (1963).

4. E. H. APPELMAN and J. G. MALM, *J. Am. Chem. Soc.*, **86**, 2141 (1964).

5. E. H. APPELMAN and J. G. MALM, *J. Am. Chem. Soc.*, **86**, 2297 (1964).

6. T. M. SPITTLER and B. JASELSKIS, *J. Am. Chem. Soc.*, **87**, 3357 (1965).

7. C. W. KOCH and S. M. WILLIAMSON, *J. Am. Chem. Soc.*, **86**, 5439 (1964).

8. *Noble-Gas Compounds*, H. H. HYMAN, Ed., Univ. of Chicago Press, 1963.

CHAPTER 9

The news about simple and stable compounds of xenon was so unexpected to chemists in 1962, and so contrary to some of their ideas about chemical bonds, that no one knew quite what to expect for the structures of the molecules. Most of the traditional techniques, as well as some of the very newest, for obtaining structural information were quickly exploited. The results of this effort are the subject of the present chapter.

The physical measurements that have proved most helpful in the determination of molecular and crystal structure over the last 30 years include the techniques of x-ray and electron diffraction and of Raman and infrared spectrometry. More recently, neutron diffraction has provided some of the information missing from x-ray results. Other more exotic measurements of the physicist, such as frequency of precession of electron or nuclear spins and the Mössbauer effect, have been used to add finer details about the nature of chemical bonds. All of these methods have been applied to xenon compounds. There is not space here to treat the theories of each of these methods. In most instances, little more than the results will be given, but the interpretation of the vibrational spectra will be discussed in some detail. To prepare for this, we digress here to consider the elements of the theory of small vibrations of molecules.

9–A THEORY OF MOLECULAR VIBRATIONS

Since more than 99.95% of the mass of a molecule is in the nuclei, we may with good accuracy treat the electrons as massless and

71

serving merely as the springs that hold the nuclei in preferred positions relative to each other. Consider a general molecule of N atoms or N mass points. Description of the possible vibratory motions of such a system is begun by writing expressions for the kinetic and potential energies of the system. Various coordinate sets might be used for this description, and we begin with familiar Cartesian coordinates. Let each atom have its own coordinate system with the origin at the equilibrium position for that atom, all the systems being parallel. Let x_1, x_2, and x_3 designate the x, y, and z displacements, respectively, of the first atom, and $m_1 = m_2 = m_3$ designate its mass. For the second atom the coordinates are designated x_4, x_5, and x_6 and the mass, $m_4 = m_5 = m_6$, and so on to $m_{n-2} = m_{n-1} = m_n$ for the mass of the last atom in the molecule where $n = 3N$, the total number of coordinates. If we let $\dot{x}_i = (dx_i/dt)$, the kinetic energy of the system is given by

$$T = (1/2) \sum_{1}^{n} m_i \dot{x}_i^2 \tag{1}$$

The potential energy presents more difficulty but it may arbitrarily be set equal to zero when all the x_i are zero, i.e., for the undistorted molecule, and it must be a function of the displacement coordinates

$$V = V(x_1, x_2, \ldots, x_n) \tag{2}$$

This may be expanded by a Taylor's series thus

$$V = \sum_{i=1}^{n} (\partial V/\partial x_i)_0 x_i + 1/2 \sum_{i=1}^{n} \sum_{j=1}^{n} (\partial^2 V/\partial x_i \, \partial x_j)_0 x_i x_j + \cdots \tag{3}$$

where the derivatives in the parentheses are to be evaluated at the equilibrium positions. The n terms of the first summation are all zero because the potential energy must be a minimum for the equilibrium positions and this means that all the first derivatives are zero. If we neglect all higher terms than those shown in Eq. (3), we are left with a quadratic form

$$V = (1/2) \sum_{i} \sum_{j} a_{ij} x_i x_j \tag{4}$$

for the potential energy where $a_{ij} = a_{ji}$. Here a_{ij} is used for the second order partial derivatives in Eq. (3). They are simply constants in the quadratic form for potential energy, and their evaluation will be discussed later. Dropping the cubic and higher terms means that this theory will be accurate only for vibrations of small amplitude.

The Lagrangian method (discussed in most undergraduate mechanics textbooks) may now be used to write differential equations of motion. Lagrange's equation

$$\frac{d}{dt}\frac{\partial(T - V)}{\partial \dot{x}_i} = \frac{\partial(T - V)}{\partial x_i} \tag{5}$$

with Equations (1) and (4) for T and V yields

$$m_i\ddot{x}_i = -\sum_{j=1}^{n} a_{ij}x_j \tag{6}$$

This is a set of n simultaneous differential equations, one for each value of i from one to n. Since the equations are similar to those for simple harmonic motion, it is reasonable to assume solutions where all atoms move with the same frequency but with different amplitudes. Assuming such a set of solutions

$$x_i = A_i \cos(2\pi\nu t + \phi) \tag{7}$$

and substituting into Eq. (6) yields a set of n equations

$$m_i A_i \lambda = \sum_j a_{ij} A_j \tag{8}$$

where $\lambda = 4\pi^2\nu^2$. More explicitly, this is written

$$(a_{11} - \lambda m_1)A_1 + a_{12}A_2 + a_{13}A_3 + \cdots + a_{1n}A_n = 0$$
$$a_{21}A_1 + (a_{22} - \lambda m_2)A_2 + a_{23}A_3 + \cdots + a_{2n}A_n = 0$$
$$\cdots$$
$$a_{n1}A_1 + a_{n2}A_2 + \cdots + (a_{nn} - \lambda m_n)A_n = 0$$

This is a set of n equations with $n + 1$ unknowns, namely λ and the amplitudes, A_i, if the a_{ij} are considered as known for the moment. It is well known from the algebra of linear equations that such a set has nontrivial solutions for the A_i only if the determinant of their coefficients is equal to zero. That is

$$\begin{vmatrix} (a_{11} - \lambda m_1) & a_{12} & \cdots & a_{1n} \\ a_{21} & (a_{22} - \lambda m_2) & \cdots & a_{2n} \\ \vdots & \vdots & & \vdots \\ a_{n1} & a_{n2} & \cdots & (a_{nn} - \lambda m_n) \end{vmatrix} = 0 \tag{9}$$

73

This equation is of degree n in λ, therefore has n solutions. Each root, λ_k may be substituted into the set (8) and the set solved for relative values of $A_i{}^k$, the superscript indicating that this set belongs to the frequency, ν_k, corresponding to $\lambda_k = 4\pi^2\nu_k{}^2$. We can make these sets definite by arbitrarily picking a value for $A_1{}^k$, so that Equations (8) yield $A_2{}^k, \ldots, A_n{}^k$ uniquely.

The equations thus allow $n = 3N$ different frequencies of vibration, and predict the relative amplitude components for each atom, $A_i{}^k$, for each frequency, ν_k. For a molecule, six (or 5 if the molecule is linear) of these motions would not be true vibrations but rather components of translational or rotational motion of the whole molecule. For these there are no restoring forces so the corresponding frequencies are zero and usually they need not be considered further. There are left $3N - 6$ (or $3N - 5$) different vibrational patterns of the molecule. For each, the atomic nuclei move with amplitudes given by components as the $A_i{}^k$ corresponding to the given ν_k.

It is convenient to define a new set of coordinates, q_k, that are linear combinations of the x_i, thus

$$q_k = A_1{}^k x_1 + A_2{}^k x_2 + \cdots + A_n{}^k x_n \tag{10}$$

since there is then a specific coordinate belonging to each frequency. The q_k are called normal coordinates, the ν_k are called normal frequencies, and a molecular vibration in which only one q_k is different from zero is called a normal mode. Vibratory motion of a given molecule may be very complicated, but it can always be described as a linear combination of normal modes.

To illustrate this theory, let us consider a very simple artificial example in which only two coordinates are involved. Two equal masses m are allowed to move along a straight line only and controlled by three weightless springs as indicated in Fig. 9.1. The two outer springs are fastened to fixed walls and have spring constant k, and the inner spring is fastened only to the masses and has constant f.

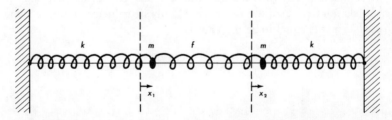

Figure 9.1 Two equal masses, spring-connected, and restricted to motion in one dimension.

Consider that all three springs exert zero forces when the masses are in the equilibrium positions, $x_1 = x_2 = 0$. Then

$$T = 0.5m(\dot{x}_1{}^2 + \dot{x}_2{}^2) \tag{11}$$

and the potential energy is in the three springs

$$
\begin{aligned}
V &= 0.5(kx_1{}^2 + kx_2{}^2 + f(x_1 - x_2)^2) \\
&= 0.5[(k + f)x_1{}^2 - fx_1x_2 - fx_2x_1 + (k + f)x_2{}^2] \tag{12}
\end{aligned}
$$

where the last is of the form of Eq. (4) with k, $-f$, and k written for a_{11}, a_{12}, and a_{22}, respectively. Corresponding to Eq. (9) we have

$$
\begin{vmatrix}
(k + f - \lambda m) & -f \\
-f & (k + f - \lambda m)
\end{vmatrix} = 0 \tag{13}
$$

with the two roots, $\lambda_1 = (k + 2f)/m$ and $\lambda_2 = k/m$, with frequencies $\nu_i = \sqrt{\lambda_i}/2\pi$. Corresponding to Eq. (8) there are two sets of equations

$$
\left.
\begin{aligned}
k + f - (k + 2f)A_1{}^1 - fA_2{}^1 &= 0 \\
-fA_1{}^1 + [k + f - (k + 2f)]A_2{}^1 &= 0
\end{aligned}
\right\} \lambda_1
$$
$$\tag{14}$$
$$
\left.
\begin{aligned}
(k + f - k)A_1{}^2 - fA_2{}^2 &= 0 \\
-fA_1{}^2 + (k + f - k)A_2{}^2 &= 0
\end{aligned}
\right\} \lambda_2
$$

with solutions (setting $A_1{}^1 = A_1{}^2 = \sqrt{0.5}$), $A_2{}^1 = -\sqrt{0.5}$, and $A_2{}^2 = +\sqrt{0.5}$. This yields the normal coordinates

$$q_1 = \sqrt{0.5}(x_1 - x_2) \quad \text{and} \quad q_2 = \sqrt{0.5}(x_1 + x_2) \tag{15}$$

If Eqs. (15) are solved for x_1 and x_2 and the results substituted into Eqs. (11) and (12) there results

$$T = 0.5m(\dot{q}_1{}^2 + \dot{q}_2{}^2) \tag{16}$$

$$V = 0.5(k + 0.5h)q_1{}^2 + kq_2{}^2 \tag{17}$$

Both of these quadratic forms contain only diagonal terms, i.e., squares of the normal coordinates, and it can be proved that this is a general characteristic of normal coordinates.

Only Cartesian coordinates have been used thus far. For these the kinetic energy can be written down very easily but the a_{ij} in the potential energy expression, Eq. (4), are mathematical constants that have meaning only for the specific problem being considered. Much preferred are sets of coordinates for a molecule composed of changes in bond lengths, Δr_i, and changes of interbond angles, $\Delta \alpha_{ij}$. Since these are internal to the molecule, they often eliminate automatically the six zero frequencies associated with translations or rotations of the molecule. The potential constants have rather direct physical meanings related to ease of deformation of lengths of bonds or angles between bonds and their values are often transferrable from one molecule to another. It is much more difficult to express the kinetic energy for such coordinates, but systematic procedures for doing so are known.

The dropping of higher than quadratic terms in Eq. (3) is a good approximation, but consideration of cubic terms, with the assumption that their contribution to energy is small, leads to new frequencies. These are to a first approximation the sums or differences of the fundamental frequencies (calculated with the quadratic assumption), and are called overtone or combination frequencies. They are commonly observed in spectra, but as a rule are much weaker than the fundamental frequencies.

Only classical mechanics has been used in this discussion, but the same expressions for kinetic and potential energies are used also in the Schroedinger equation. Solution of this equation involves consideration of the same secular Eq. (9), and the possible vibrational energies of the molecule in the quadratic approximation are

$$W = \sum_k (v_k + 0.5)h\nu_k \qquad \textbf{(18)}$$

Here the ν_k are the same frequencies as in the classical problem and the v_k are quantum numbers restricted to integers. Possible changes in molecular vibrational energies are restricted to amounts of $h\nu_k$ times an integer.

The molecular spectroscopist observes the vibrational frequencies of a molecule by means of infrared absorption and of Raman spectra. From these he attempts to obtain structural information and also to evaluate constants in the potential function. If a molecule has symmetry, certain of its normal frequencies may be observable only in the infrared spectrum, others only in the Raman spectrum, others in both, and still others in neither.

For most chemical bonds there is an electric dipole moment along, or approximately along, the bond length because the two electrons primarily involved in the bond spend a larger fraction of their time

76

near one of the atoms than near the other. Changing the bond length generally causes a change in the dipole moment. For a normal vibration of a molecule, several bonds are usually changing their lengths or relative directions. If, between the two extremes of the normal vibration, the total dipole moment of the molecule changes either its magnitude or its direction, the molecule will exchange energy with an electromagnetic wave of the same frequency, i.e., it will absorb energy from a beam of infrared light of frequency equal to that of the normal vibration. In terms of light quanta, there is a selection rule, $\Delta v_k = \pm 1$, so that the molecule may absorb or re-emit an energy $h\nu_k$ only if its dipole moment changes with the kth normal vibration.

The Raman effect depends on scattering of light, usually in the visible part of the spectrum. All molecules scatter light because their electrons are forced into a vibratory motion by the electric field of the radiation, and this electronic motion radiates light into new directions. For ordinary field strengths, the induced dipole moment of a molecule is a linear function of field, thus

$$\mathbf{p} = \alpha \mathbf{E} \tag{19}$$

where α is called the polarizability. It is a constant for a molecule with cubic symmetry, but in general is a symmetrical tensor. When the molecule is distorted from its equilibrium configuration the components of α will change their magnitude. If α is different at the two extremes of a normal vibration this vibration will show up in the Raman spectrum. This is because α must depend on the normal coordinate, q, and in the Taylor's expansion, the first derivative is nonzero. Thus

$$\alpha = \alpha_0 + \frac{\partial \alpha}{\partial q} q + \cdots \tag{20}$$

$$= \alpha_0 + \beta q_m \cos 2\pi \nu t$$

where β is written for the derivative, q_m is the amplitude, and ν is the frequency of the normal vibration. If E in Eq. (18) is the field of monochromatic light of frequency f and amplitude E_m, then Eq. (19) becomes

$$\mathbf{p} = (\alpha_0 + \beta q_m \cos 2\pi \nu t)(\mathbf{E}_m \cos 2\pi f t)$$

$$= \alpha_0 \mathbf{E}_m \cos 2\pi f t + 0.5 \beta q_m \mathbf{E}_m \cos 2\pi (f + \nu) t \tag{21}$$

$$+ 0.5 \beta q_m \mathbf{E}_m \cos 2\pi (f - \nu) t$$

This shows that the scattered light will contain not only the incident frequency, f, but also two new frequencies, $f + \nu$ and $f - \nu$. In

Raman spectroscopy observations are often limited to the difference frequencies, molecular frequencies being determined by subtraction from the incident frequency.

In terms of quanta, the Raman effect is viewed as a scattering in which a vibrational quantum of energy is either subtracted from or added to the scattered photon. Thus the incident energy is hf and the scattered photon energy is either $h(f - v)$ or $h(f + v)$. The former is more probable, however, because there are generally more molecules in the lowest vibrational level than in the excited level. Thus the majority of molecules can take energy from the photon, but only a minority can add to it. This prediction from quantum theory is in agreement with experiment, since the sum frequencies are always weaker than the difference frequencies. The classical theory leading to Eq. (21) is not adequate in this respect.

The vibrational spectra are complicated in practice because molecules of a gas have translational and rotational motions as well as vibrational. The first has little effect on spectra but rotational energies may be added to or subtracted from vibrational energies. Since rotational frequencies are small compared to vibrational, the effect in spectra is the broadening of a vibrational "line" to a vibrational-rotational "band" (which may, however, be resolved into many lines at high resolution). The rotational energies are quantized and infrared bands often have three absorption maxima called P, Q, and R branches for the three allowed changes in rotational quantum number, ΔJ, of -1, 0, and $+1$, respectively. Q branches are commonly rather sharp but P and R branches are relatively broad because rotational energy is proportional to J^2 and change in energy, therefore, to J. Molecules of a gas have various J values, hence change their energies by different amounts when J changes by $+1$. The shapes of infrared bands depend on the thermal populations and statistical weights of the various rotational levels, and the shapes often help to identify observed bands with specific normal vibrations.

Even if all $(3N - 6)$ normal frequencies of a molecule are evaluated from the spectra, and if the general shape of the molecule is known, it is usually not possible to determine the potential constants uniquely, because the general molecule with N atoms has only $3N - 6 = n$ vibrational frequencies, but has $n(n + 1)/2$ potential constants. For three frequencies the number of a_{ij} is 6, for four it is 10 and so on. The situation is better if the molecule has symmetry, for then some of the potential constants must be equal to each other and there are fewer independent ones to evaluate. Even so, more vibrational frequencies are usually needed and are sometimes obtainable from isotopically substituted molecules or from very similar molecules.

This very brief introduction to molecular spectra has omitted a number of important aspects of the theory. Some of these are taken up below as needed for specific molecules. For a general and detailed treatment, however, the student is referred to the two books by Herzberg (1) and, if he has knowledge of group theory and matrix algebra, to Wilson, Decius and Cross (2).

9–B STRUCTURES OF XeF_2 AND KrF_2

When the first description of xenon tetrafluoride was published, some evidence for a lower fluoride was mentioned. Smith (3) followed this suggestion, mixed xenon and fluorine in a system including a cell with transparent windows, caused a reaction by heating part of the system, and observed the infrared spectrum of the mixture. From the two infrared absorption bands that were observed he concluded that a compound with formula XeF_2 was present, that the gaseous molecule was linear, with the xenon atom midway between the fluorine atoms, obtained an approximate value for the bond length, and evaluated two force constants for the quadratic potential function. To see how this was possible we examine the vibrational pattern for the symmetric, linear YZ_2 molecule.

It is convenient to use the internal coordinates r_1, r_2, α_1, α_2 as shown in Fig. 9.2. There α_1 is considered to be in the plane of the paper and α_2 in the perpendicular plane. The general quadratic form for the potential energy in terms of these coordinates is

$$2V = k_r(\Delta r_1{}^2 + \Delta r_2{}^2) + r^2 k_\alpha(\Delta\alpha_1{}^2 + \Delta\alpha_2{}^2) + 2k_{rr}\Delta r_1\Delta r_2$$
$$+ 2r^2 k_{\alpha\alpha}\Delta\alpha_1\Delta\alpha_2 + 2rk_{r\alpha}(\Delta r_1\Delta\alpha_1 + \Delta r_1\Delta\alpha_2$$
$$+ \Delta r_2\Delta\alpha_1 + \Delta r_2\Delta\alpha_2) \tag{22}$$

where Δr means deviation of bond length from the equilibrium value r, and $\Delta\alpha$ means deviation from the equilibrium value π. Of the five force constants k_i, appearing here, the last two can be set equal to

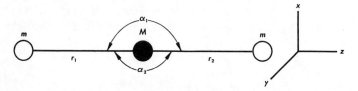

Figure 9.2 Coordinates used to describe vibrations of YZ_2 molecules.

79

zero from considerations based on symmetry. For example, consider the term $2r^2k_{\alpha\alpha}\,\Delta\alpha_1\,\Delta\alpha_2$ when $\Delta r_1 = \Delta r_2 = 0$ and $\Delta\alpha_1 = \Delta\alpha_2 = \epsilon$, compared to $\Delta r_1 = \Delta r_2 = 0$, $\Delta\alpha_2 = \epsilon$, and $\Delta\alpha_1 = -\epsilon$. The potential energy must obviously be the same for $\Delta\alpha_1$ increasing and decreasing by the amount ϵ, and this can be true only for $k_{\alpha\alpha} = 0$. We are left, then, with the three-constant function

$$2V = k_r(\Delta r_1{}^2 + \Delta r_2{}^2) + r^2k_\alpha(\Delta\alpha_1{}^2 + \Delta\alpha_2{}^2) + 2k_{rr}\,\Delta r_1\,\Delta r_2 \quad \textbf{(23)}$$

To express the kinetic energy in terms of these internal coordinates, we begin with Cartesian displacement coordinates, x_i, y_i, z_i, where i is 1 for the left atom, 2 for the right atom, and 3 for the central atom. The kinetic energy is obviously

$$2T = m(\dot{x}_1{}^2 + \dot{y}_1{}^2 + \dot{z}_1{}^2 + \dot{x}_2{}^2 + \dot{y}_2{}^2 + \dot{z}_2{}^2) + M(\dot{x}_3{}^2 + \dot{y}_3{}^2 + \dot{z}_3{}^2)$$
$$\textbf{(24)}$$

but it must also be expressible as a quadratic form in the time derivatives of the internal coordinates, thus

$$2T = A(\Delta\dot{r}_1{}^2 + \Delta\dot{r}_2{}^2) + B(\Delta\dot{\alpha}_1{}^2 + \Delta\dot{\alpha}_2{}^2) + 2C\,\Delta\dot{r}_1\,\Delta\dot{r}_2 + 2D\,\Delta\dot{\alpha}_1\,\Delta\dot{\alpha}_2$$
$$+ 2E(\Delta\dot{r}_1\,\Delta\dot{\alpha}_1 + \Delta\dot{r}_1\,\Delta\dot{\alpha}_2 + \Delta\dot{r}_2\,\Delta\dot{\alpha}_1 + \Delta\dot{r}_2\,\Delta\dot{\alpha}_2) \quad \textbf{(25)}$$

To evaluate the coefficients in Eq. (25) we assign arbitrary velocities to the atoms so as to permit easy comparisons between Eqs. (24) and (25).

Since we are interested in internal motions we restrict these velocity assignments to combinations such that both the angular and linear momenta of the molecule as a whole are zero. For example, the velocity pattern, $\dot{x}_1 = \dot{x}_2 = v$, $\dot{x}_3 = -(2m/M)v$, with all other components zero has total linear momentum $= 2mv - (2m/M)vM = 0$ and has $\Delta\dot{r}_1 = \Delta\dot{r}_2 = \Delta\dot{\alpha}_2 = 0$ and $\Delta\dot{\alpha}_1 = 2(M + 2m)v/Mr$, provided the displacements are small. Substitution into Eqs. (24) and (25) yields $B = mMr^2/2(M + 2m)$. Similarly one finds $A = m(M + m)/(M + 2m)$, $C = m^2/(M + 2m)$, and $D = E = 0$. This simplifies Eq. (25) to only three different coefficients but it must be reduced to a sum of squares to be like Eq. (1), the prototype for the above theory. To do this we remember an algebraic identity, $ab = (a + b)^2/2 + (a - b)^2/2$, and define a new set of variables

$$S_1 = (\Delta r_1 + \Delta r_2)/\sqrt{2}$$
$$S_{2a} = \Delta\alpha_1$$
$$S_{2b} = \Delta\alpha_2 \quad \textbf{(26)}$$
$$S_3 = (\Delta r_1 - \Delta r_2)\sqrt{2}$$

Substitution yields immediately

$$2T = m\dot{S}_1^{\,2} + \frac{r^2 mM}{2(M + 2m)}(\dot{S}_{2a}^{\,2} + \dot{S}_{2b}^{\,2}) + \frac{mM}{M + 2m}\dot{S}_3^{\,2} \quad \textbf{(27)}$$

$$2V = (k_r + k_{rr})S_1^{\,2} + r^2 k_\alpha(S_{2a}^{\,2} + S_{2b}^{\,2}) + (k_r - k_{rr})S_3^{\,2} \quad \textbf{(28)}$$

The determinant of Eq. (9) for this case has all nondiagonal terms equal to zero, and its value is the product of the four diagonal terms. Each of these may be set equal to zero in turn to give the possible values for λ or for the frequency ν. The results are

$$\begin{aligned}
4\pi^2\nu_1^{\,2} &= \lambda_1 = (k_r + k_{rr})/m \\
4\pi^2\nu_2^{\,2} &= \lambda_2 = 2k_\alpha(M + 2m)/mM \quad \textbf{(29)} \\
4\pi^2\nu_3^{\,2} &= \lambda_3 = (k_r - k_{rr})(M + 2m)/mM
\end{aligned}$$

Comparison with Eqs. (8), (9), and (10) shows that the coordinates, S_i, of Eqs. (26) are the normal coordinates for the molecule. The molecule has only three distinct frequencies, since ν_2 pertains, of course, to either S_{2a} or S_{2b}, which are said to be a degenerate pair. This is an unusually fortunate case in that knowledge of the frequencies permits a unique calculation of force constants.

Figure 9.3 pictures the displacements for the normal vibrational modes. The spectral activities in absorption may be inferred from this figure by assuming that each of the two bonds has a dipole moment from the end atom toward the central atom and that the magnitude of this changes with bond length. For the motion associated with ν_1 the two dipole moments are always opposite and add to zero, and so ν_1 is inactive in absorption. For ν_2, the two dipoles

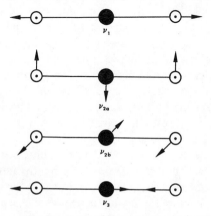

Figure 9.3 The normal vibrations of linear, symmetric YZ_2 molecules.

do not remain parallel and there is a vector sum perpendicular to the molecular axis that is oscillating from one direction to the opposite, and this motion will show up in absorption. For ν_3, there is a dipole moment of the molecule oscillating along the molecular axis since one bond moment is increasing while the opposite one is decreasing, and so this also is active in absorption.

The Raman effect depends not on dipole moment, but on polarizability. For either ν_2 or ν_3, the polarizability must evidently be the same at the two extremes of the motion, and so both are inactive. For ν_1, however, the polarizability will be different at one extreme of the motion than at the other, and so it is active in the Raman spectrum. These conclusions provide an example of a general selection rule for all molecules with a center of symmetry, that says any vibration active in absorption is inactive in the Raman effect, and vice versa.

Detailed treatments show that for ν_3 the further selection rule, $\Delta J = \pm 1$, applies, but for ν_2, ΔJ may be ± 1 or 0. Thus ν_2 will have P, Q, and R branches, but ν_3 will have only P and R branches.

When Smith (3) studied the infrared spectrum of his unknown xenon fluoride in the region where bond-stretching frequencies for XeF_4 had been observed, he found one intense band, centered at $558\ cm^{-1}$, with well separated P and R branches and with no Q branch. The observed data, namely, only one infrared band in the bond-stretching region and that with missing Q branch, fit perfectly the predictions above for a linear, symmetric XeF_2 molecule. A bent triatomic molecule could be ruled out because it should have two bands, both with Q branches. The lack of a Q branch could rule out other likely molecules, but not the possibility of a diatomic molecule, XeF, which would have only one fundamental vibrational frequency. A second, weak, absorption band at $1070\ cm^{-1}$, however, was interpreted as the combination band, $\nu_1 + \nu_3$, for XeF_2, and the frequency was too low to be the overtone, 2ν, for a possible XeF.

The spacing between the maxima of the P and R branches of the $558\ cm^{-1}$ band was used to calculate a moment of inertia and thus, a bond length for the gaseous XeF_2 molecule. This was first given as 1.7 Å, but was later restudied more carefully with a resulting value of 1.9 Å (5, p. 295).

The frequency, ν_1, was evaluated by subtracting ν_3 from the combination frequency at $1070\ cm^{-1}$. Smith and coworkers (4) later gave $555\ cm^{-1}$ for ν_3, calculated $515\ cm^{-1}$ for ν_1, and observed $213.2\ cm^{-1}$ for ν_2, the last having the expected sharp Q branch. The symmetrical vibration, v_1, was also verified by observation of the Raman spectrum.

KrF_2 was recently studied in some detail at Argonne (6). The fundamentals, v_2 and v_3, and the combinations, $v_1 + v_3$, were observed in the infrared spectrum and v_1 was observed in the Raman spectrum of the vapor. Again, the spectra unambiguously indicated linear, symmetric molecules.

The force constants for both molecules were evaluated with Eqs. (29). In using Eqs. (29) or similar ones given later it must be remembered that v_i in the equations refers to frequencies in cycles/sec, but the numbers for v_i usually used by spectroscopists are frequencies divided by the velocity of light, thus in cycles/cm or simply cm^{-1}. The vibrational frequencies and force constants are summarized in Table IX.1.

Table IX.1

Frequencies and Force Constants for XeF_2 and KrF_2

Molecule	Frequency (cm^{-1})			Force Constants ($m\ dy/\text{Å}$)		
	v_1	v_2	v_3	k_r	k_{rr}	k_α
XeF_2	515	213.2	555	2.82	0.15	0.19
KrF_2	449	232.6	588	2.46	−0.20	0.21

It is worth noting, in passing, that these frequencies, force constants and bond lengths are of the same order of magnitude as for the iodine or bromine fluorides, thus indicating that the chemical binding is similar.

Both x-ray and neutron diffraction methods have been applied to the structure determination of solid XeF_2. Siegel and Gebert (7) used x-rays to determine that the unit cell was tetragonal and that the xenon atoms wete at the corners and body centers of the cells. The fluorine atoms were located only approximately because x-rays are scattered by the electrons and the intense scattering by the 54 xenon electrons tends to mask that of the eighteen fluorine electrons. Neutrons, on the other hand, are scattered by nuclei and the fluorine and xenon are nearly equal in scattering power. Levy and Agron (5, p. 221), (8) studied a single crystal of XeF_2 about, 1.5 × 1.0 × 0.5 mm, for ten days with a neutron beam made monochromatic at 1.078 Å by crystal reflection. Their automatic scanning apparatus measured diffracted intensities for 90 different *hkl* (Miller indices for sets of parallel planes) reflections. The structure corresponding to these data was refined by iterative least squares using an IBM 7090. The molecules were found to be linear and symmetric, as had been found for the gas, and were all parallel and aligned with the tetrad axes as shown in Fig. 9.4. The xenon and fluorine positions within molecules were separated by 1.984 Å with a least squares standard error of 0.004 Å. The fluorine and xenon positions were blurred by thermal motions, and correction for this yielded a bond length of 2.00 ± 0.01 Å. Distances between nonbonded atoms were all 50% or more greater than this, as indicated in the figure.

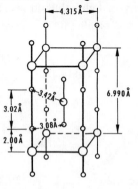

O =Xe   o=F

Figure 9.4 Crystal structure of XeF_2 according to Levy and Agron. Taken from Science, *139*, 843 (1963). The cell dimensions are from Siegel and Gebert (7).

All the xenon fluorides were studied by magnetic resonance of the fluorine nuclei by Hindman and Svirmickas (5, p. 251). Some of their conclusions relative to binding orbitals are discussed in the next chapter. Here it may suffice to note that both for solid XeF_2 and for its solution in HF the measurements gave support for the equivalence of the two fluorines in the molecule. The chemical shifts were 612 × 10^{-6} for the solid and 629 × 10^{-6} for the solution, both relative to the F_2 molecule. This shift is about equal to that for the fluorine in liquid HF, and was interpreted to indicate a formal charge of $-0.7e$ on each of the fluorine atoms.

9–C STRUCTURES OF XeF_4 AND $XeOF_4$

When the first xenon fluoride was prepared, its infrared spectrum was immediately studied to help establish the nature of the compound.

An intense absorption band was found centered at 586 cm^{-1}; in the same frequency region where bond-stretching vibrations were known to occur for iodine fluorides. A single infrared-active bond-stretching frequency for the XeF_4 molecule meant that it had high symmetry. In fact, only for the fluorines at the corners of a regular tetrahedron or at the corners of a plane square would the selection rules allow just one such frequency. A study of the Raman spectrum definitely ruled out the tetrahedral model. The molecules, CH_4, CF_4, and nearly all other YZ_4 molecules were known to be tetrahedral, and XeF_4 proved to be the first molecule with the plane square configuration. There were a few ionic antecedents: $(ICl_4)^-$, for example, was known to be plane square in certain crystals.

The vibrational motions of a planar YZ_4 molecule may be described conveniently by means of the ten coordinates defined in Fig. 9.5.

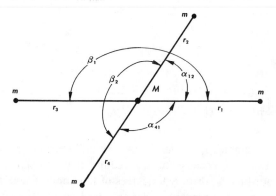

Figure 9.5 Internal coordinates used for XeF_4.

The four angles, α_{ij}, are in the molecular plane and the two angles, β_i, have the equilibrium value of π and measure bending motions perpendicular to the plane. The quadratic potential energy function may be given in terms of nine potential constants

$$
\begin{aligned}
2V = {} & k_r(\Delta r_1{}^2 + \Delta r_2{}^2 + \Delta r_3{}^2 + \Delta r_4{}^2) + r^2 k\alpha(\Delta \alpha_1{}^2 + \Delta \alpha_2{}^2 + \Delta \alpha_3{}^2 \\
& + \Delta \alpha_4{}^2) + r^2 k\beta(\Delta \beta_1{}^2 + \Delta \beta_2{}^2) + 2k_{rr}(\Delta r_1 \Delta r_2 + \Delta r_2 \Delta r_3 + \Delta r_3 \Delta r_4 \\
& + \Delta r_4 \Delta r_1) + 2r^2 k_{\alpha\alpha}(\Delta \alpha_{12} \Delta \alpha_{23} + \Delta \alpha_{23} \Delta \alpha_{34} + \Delta \alpha_{34} \Delta \alpha_{41} \\
& + \Delta \alpha_{41} \Delta \alpha_{12}) + 2rk_{r\alpha}(\Delta r_1 \Delta \alpha_{12} + \Delta r_1 \Delta \alpha_{41} + \Delta r_2 \Delta \alpha_{23} + \Delta r_2 \Delta \alpha_{12} \\
& + \Delta r_3 \Delta \alpha_{34} + \Delta r_3 \Delta \alpha_{23} + \Delta r_4 \Delta \alpha_{41} + \Delta r_4 \Delta \alpha_{34}) + 2k'_{rr}(\Delta r_1 \Delta r_3 \\
& + \Delta r_2 \Delta r_4) + 2r^2 k'_{\alpha\alpha}(\Delta \alpha_{12} \Delta \alpha_{34} + \Delta \alpha_{23} \Delta \alpha_{41}) + 2r^2 k_{\beta\beta} \Delta \beta_1 \Delta \beta_2 \\
& + 2rk'_{r\alpha}(\Delta r_1 \Delta \alpha_{23} + \Delta r_1 \Delta \alpha_{34} + \Delta r_2 \Delta \alpha_{34} + \Delta r_2 \Delta \alpha_{41} + \Delta r_3 \Delta \alpha_{12} \\
& + \Delta r_3 \Delta \alpha_{41} + \Delta r_4 \Delta \alpha_{12} + \Delta r_4 \Delta \alpha_{23})
\end{aligned}
\tag{30}
$$

Here the cross product terms are all included except those between β_i and α_{ij} or between β_i and r_i. The coefficients for these can be seen to be zero by noting that the potential energy cannot change if $-\beta_i$ is substituted for β_i unless β_j is different from zero also. Details of writing the kinetic energy function and of finding coordinates appropriate to the normal vibrations will not be given here. The student is referred again to Refs. (1) and (2). The ten symmetry coordinates most appropriate are

$$
\begin{aligned}
S_0(a_{1g}) &= 0.5(\Delta\alpha_{12} + \Delta\alpha_{23} + \Delta\alpha_{34} + \Delta\alpha_{41}) = 0 \\
S_1(a_{1g}) &= 0.5(\Delta r_1 + \Delta r_2 + \Delta r_3 + \Delta r_4) \\
S_2(a_{2u}) &= (1/\sqrt{2})(\Delta\beta_1 + \Delta\beta_2) \\
S_3(b_{1g}) &= 0.5(\Delta\alpha_{12} - \Delta\alpha_{23} + \Delta\alpha_{34} - \Delta\alpha_{41}) \\
S_4(b_{1u}) &= (1/\sqrt{2})(\Delta\beta_1 - \Delta\beta_2) \\
S_5(b_{2g}) &= 0.5(\Delta r_1 - \Delta r_2 + \Delta r_3 - \Delta r_4) \\
S_{6a}(e_u) &= 0.5(\Delta r_1 - \Delta r_2 - \Delta r_3 + \Delta r_4) \\
S_{6b}(e_u) &= 0.5(\Delta r_1 + \Delta r_2 - \Delta r_3 - \Delta r_4) \\
S_{7a}(e_u) &= (1/\sqrt{2})(\Delta\alpha_{23} - \Delta\alpha_{41}) \\
S_{7b}(e_u) &= (1/\sqrt{2})(\Delta\alpha_{12} - \Delta\alpha_{34})
\end{aligned}
\tag{31}
$$

The first coordinate, S_0, is identically zero and need not be considered further. It arises because of the redundancy associated with ten internal coordinates for only 9 degrees of freedom. The designations such as a_{1g}, etc. in parentheses are standard group theoretical notations for the particular symmetry of the displacement pattern suggested by the coordinate. The last four coordinates are degenerate pairs of the same symmetry and represent only two different frequencies. The determinantal equation, (Eq. 9), now factors into seven equations

$$
\begin{aligned}
a_{1g} \qquad & m\lambda_1 = k_r + k'_{rr} + 2k_{rr} \\[4pt]
a_{2u} \qquad & m\lambda_2 = 2(k_\beta + k_{\beta\beta})\left(1 + \frac{4m}{M}\right) \\[4pt]
b_{1g} \qquad & m\lambda_3 = 4k_\alpha + 4k'_{\alpha\alpha} - 8k_{\alpha\alpha} \\[4pt]
b_{1u} \qquad & m\lambda_4 = 2(k_\beta - k_{\beta\beta}) \\[4pt]
b_{2g} \qquad & m\lambda_5 = k_r + k'_{rr} - 2k_{rr}
\end{aligned}
$$

$$e_u \begin{cases} m\lambda_6 m\lambda_7 = 2\left(1 + \frac{4m}{M}\right)\left[(k_r - k'_{rr})(k_\alpha - k'_{\alpha\alpha}) - 2(k'_{r\alpha} - k_{r\alpha})^2\right] \\ m\lambda_6 + m\lambda_7 = \left(1 + \frac{2m}{M}\right)(k_r - k'_{rr}) + 2\left(1 + \frac{2m}{M}\right)(k_\alpha - k'_{\alpha\alpha}) \end{cases}$$

$$+ \frac{8m}{M}(k'_{r\alpha} - k_{r\alpha}) \qquad \textbf{(32)}$$

Here M is the mass of the central atom and m the mass of one of the other four.

XeF$_4$				XeOF$_4$			
				R,p	919s	ν_1	a_1 
				IR	928.2s		
 a_{1g} ν_1	R	543vs		R,p	566vs	ν_2	a_1 
				IR	578 ?vw		
 a_{2u} ν_2	IR	291s		R	286vw	ν_3	a_1 
				IR	288s		
 b_{1g} ν_3	R	235w		R	231w	ν_4	b_1 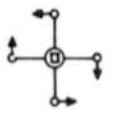
 b_{2g} ν_5	R	502vs		R	530s	ν_5	b_2 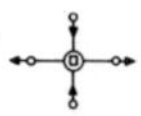
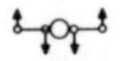 b_{1u} ν_4	Inactive	221??		R	n.o.	ν_6	b_2 
 e_u ν_6	IR	586vs		R	n.o.	ν_7	e
				IR	609vs		
				R	364mw	ν_8	e
				IR	362ms		
 e_u ν_7	IR	n.o.		R	n.o.	ν_9	e 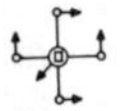
				IR	n.o.		
$\nu_5 + \nu_6$	IR	1105w		IR	1186w	$\nu_2 + \nu_7$	
$\nu_1 + \nu_6$	IR	1136w		IR	1156w	$2\nu_2$	
				IR	735w	$2\nu_8$ and /or $\nu_7 + \nu_9$ and/or $\nu_5 + \nu_6$	
				R	818w	$\nu_3 + \nu_5$	

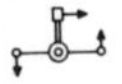

Figure 9.6 Vibrational modes and assignments for XeF$_4$ and XeOF$_4$. From Ref. 5, p. 290.

The left-hand column of Fig. 9.6 shows the vibrational patterns associated with the seven different frequencies, although the last two

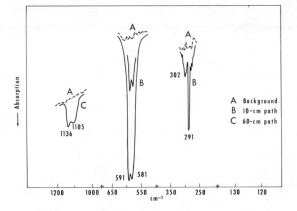

Figure 9.7 Infrared spectrum of XeF_4 vapor. From Ref. 5, p. 289.

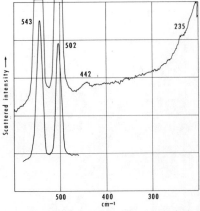

Figure 9.8 Raman spectrum of solid XeF_4. From Ref. 5, p. 289.

may be mixed to some extent. From the displacement diagrams it is immediately obvious that ν_2, ν_6, and ν_7 will be active in absorption and that ν_1 will be Raman-active. That ν_3 and ν_5 are also Raman-active follows from the fact that the direction of easiest polarization rotates 90° between the extremes of the vibration. The displacement pattern for ν_4 is a puckering of the square and this frequency is inactive in both spectra.

Figures 9.7 and 9.8 show, respectively, infrared and Raman spectra of XeF_4 obtained by Claassen, Chernick and Malm (5, p. 289). The most intense infrared absorption centered at 586 cm^{-1} must be assigned to ν_6, the only allowed bond-stretching motion. The band at 291 cm^{-1} must be assigned to ν_2 because the detailed theory predicts an intense Q branch only for ν_2. The infrared band given at 123 cm^{-1} in Ref. (5, p. 289) and assigned to ν_7 is deleted here

88

because further work by Chernick and the author has shown that it was due to an impurity. The weak absorption bands at 1105 and 1136 cm^{-1} are assigned as $\nu_5 + \nu_6$ and $\nu_1 + \nu_6$.

The Raman spectrum for the solid shows two very intense bands at 543 and 502 cm^{-1} that can be assigned to ν_1 and ν_5, respectively. From the combination infrared bands mentioned above, these frequencies are calculated as 550 and 519 cm^{-1}. The discrepancy is primarily due to changes in vibrational frequencies as the molecules are condensed to the solid phase. Hyman and Quarterman found a value of 551 cm^{-1} for ν_1 in the Raman spectrum of a solution of XeF_4 in HF (5, p. 278), in excellent agreement with the vapor value. The Raman band at 235 cm^{-1} must represent a bending frequency, hence is clearly identified as ν_3. The second and fourth of Equations (32) allow an approximate calculation of ν_4, the inactive frequency, from the observed value of ν_2 and the assumption that $k_{\beta\beta}$ is very small compared to k_β. The result of this is 232 cm^{-1} for ν_4, but this calculation must not be considered as an accurate one. The experimental value of 221 for ν_4 listed in Fig. 9.6 is obtained by considering the 442 cm^{-1} Raman band to be the overtone, $2\nu_4$, which is allowed in the Raman effect. The reality of the observed 442 cm^{-1} is in doubt, however. The peak may represent the 543 and 502 vibrations excited by two weaker mercury lines near the main exciting line at 4358 Å. Probably the best value for ν_4 is the calculated one of 232 cm^{-1}.

Even if ν_7 for XeF_4 is observed, it will not be possible to determine all force constants of Eq. (30). A few that can be determined without knowledge of ν_7 are

$$k_r + k'_{rr} = 3.20 \text{ millidynes/Å}$$
$$k_{rr} = 0.09 \text{ millidynes/Å} \qquad \textbf{(33)}$$
$$k_\beta + k_{\beta\beta} = 0.30 \text{ millidynes/Å}$$
$$k_\alpha + k'_{\alpha\alpha} - 2k_{\alpha\alpha} = 0.155 \text{ millidynes/Å}$$

The interaction constant for opposite bonds, k'_{rr}, may be approximately equal to the similar constant for XeF_2. This would lead to 3.05 millidynes/Å for the bond-stretching constant, still significantly higher than the 2.82 found for XeF_2.

Even though two of the seven fundamentals of XeF_4 are not observed, the vibrational spectra fit perfectly into the expected pattern for a plane square model and thus serve to establish that shape for the molecule. The Q-R separation in the infrared spectrum of ν_2 is 11 ± 1 cm^{-1} for the room temperature vapor. This can be used to calculate 1.85 ± 0.20 Å for the Xe-F bond length.

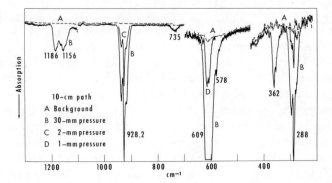

Figure 9.9 Infrared spectrum of XeOF₄ vapor. From Ref. 5, p. 292.

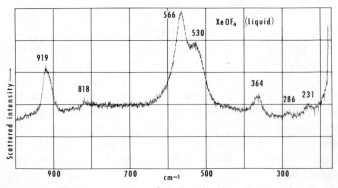

Figure 9.10 Raman spectrum of XeOF₄ liquid. From Ref. 5, p. 292.

Figures 9.9 and 9.10 show, respectively, the infrared spectrum of the vapor and Raman spectrum of the liquid for $XeOF_4$. Details will be left out, but the right half of Fig. 9.6 shows the shape of the molecule, the approximate patterns of the nine normal vibrational modes, and the frequency assignment. This molecule has no center of symmetry and six of the frequencies are allowed in both spectra. The other three are allowed in the Raman spectrum.

As Claassen, Chernick and Malm pointed out (5, p. 293), "there is a close correspondence between the vibrations of XeF_4 and those of $XeOF_4$. Each vibration of XeF_4 has a corresponding one in $XeOF_4$, and the latter has two additional ones. There is only one pair, however, for which frequencies can be compared directly between the two molecules, because only for ν_3 in XeF_4 and ν_4 in $XeOF_4$ do we have comparable motions, and each is the only vibration

90

in the species so that there are no interactions with other vibrations. For this pair we have 235 cm^{-1} for solid XeF$_4$ and 231 cm^{-1} for liquid XeOF$_4$, i.e., essentially the same frequency. Intensity comparisons provide further confirmation for the close correspondence. Thus, ν_2 for XeOF$_4$ is very strong in the Raman and very weak in the infrared, and the corresponding motion in XeF$_4$ is allowed only in the Raman spectrum. In XeOF$_4$, ν_6, ν_7, and ν_9 are all allowed in the Raman effect but not observed, presumably because they are very weak. The three corresponding motions in XeF$_4$ are all forbidden in the Raman effect. These observations indicate that the XeF$_4$ part of the XeOF$_4$ has very nearly the same configuration as the XeF$_4$ molecule. Thus the O-Xe-F angle must be rather near 90°, although the symmetry does not require 90°, and repulsion between the oxygen and the fluorines could well cause a larger angle."

Smith (5, p. 302) assumed an O-Xe-F angle of 90° and calculated force constants of 3.20 millidynes/Å for the Xe-F bond and 7.10 for the Xe-O bond. This value for the former is identical to that given above for XeF$_4$, again emphasizing the similarity. Martins and Wilson (9) very recently studied the pure rotational spectrum of XeOF$_4$ in the microwave region, and confirmed the general shape of the molecule. They gave 1.70 Å for the Xe-O bond length, 1.95 Å for the Xe-F and 91 $\pm$ 2° for the O-Xe-F angle.

XeF$_4$ vapor was also studied by means of electron diffraction by Bohn and co-workers (5, p. 238). From the scattering intensity of 45,000 volt electrons as a function of angle, they calculated a radial distribution function. This showed a principal peak at 1.94 Å for the Xe-F distances, and minor peaks at 2.77 and 3.88 Å for F-F distances. These are best interpreted in terms of a plane, square molecule of bond length, 1.94 Å. This is in good agreement with the infrared results.

Four groups of workers reported results of x-ray diffraction studies of solid XeF$_4$ at nearly the same time. Siegel and Gebert (7) first reported a monoclinic unit cell for the crystal with axes, 5.03, 5.92, and 5.79 Å and angle of 99°27'. Again, neutron diffraction was used to locate the fluorines precisely in the unit cell. Burns, Agron and Levy (10) (5, p. 211) collected neutron diffraction data from a single crystal of about 25 mg for a whole month. All symmetry-independent reflections out to $\sin \theta = 0.76\lambda$ were recorded. The molecule in the crystal was found to be plane by symmetry, the interbond angles were evaluated as 90.0 $\pm$ 0.1° and the Xe-F bond lengths, after correction for thermal motions, were found equal at 1.95 $\pm$ 0.01 Å.

Thus the shape and size of the molecule is very precisely retained in the crystalline state. No diffraction data have yet been published on $XeOF_4$.

Nuclear magnetic resonances have been studied for XeF_4 crystals and for solutions in HF, and $XeOF_4$ was studied both as liquid and as solid (5, p. 251). The chemical shift of F-19 was 482 and 454 $\times$ 10^{-6} relative to F_2 for crystalline and dissolved XeF_4 and was 326×10^{-6} for $XeOF_4$. The data were interpreted to indicate charges on the fluorines of $-0.55e$ for XeF_4 and $-0.4e$ for $XeOF_4$.

9–D STRUCTURE OF XeF_6

Much has been said, in the way of predictions, about the shape of the XeF_6 molecule, but no definite conclusion can be given from experimental studies as yet. This is not because of lack of effort. On the contrary, determination of the molecular structure of XeF_6 has had a high priority in several laboratories for more than a year. The lack of success for this long a time may, in part, be due to unique properties of the molecule, but is largely due to the difficulty of containing the material in pure form. It reacts rapidly with materials commonly used as windows for infrared spectra and as capillaries for diffraction studies.

Before the preparation of XeF_6, the hexafluorides of fifteen other elements (S, Se, Te, Mo, Tc, Ru, Rh, W, Re, Os, Ir, Pt, U, Np, and Pu) had been investigated. Infrared spectra have been reported for all of them, and all are considered to have vapor phase molecules with the fluorines at the corners of a regular octahedron. If XeF_6 has the same structure it would mean a continuation of the trend from XeF_2 through XeF_4 of linear F-Xe-F pairs of bonds along mutually perpendicular directions. Some theoretical chemists have predicted this for XeF_6, but others have predicted a less symmetrical structure.

For the symmetrical YZ_6 molecule there are 15 degrees of freedom but four of the normal vibrations are triply degenerate, so there are only six vibrational frequencies. Two bond-stretching motions, ν_1 and ν_2, are Raman-active and one, ν_3, is infrared-active. These would be expected for XeF_6 between 500 and 700 cm^{-1}. The other three are bending motions expected between 100 and 300 cm^{-1}. Of these, ν_4 is infrared-active, ν_5 is Raman-active, and ν_6 is inactive in both spectra. For any other molecular structure than this highly symmetrical one, there would be more Raman and infrared funda-

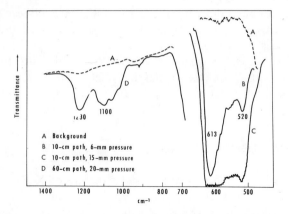

Figure 9.11 Infrared spectrum of XeF$_6$ vapor. From Ref. 11.

mentals, and the total number of normal frequencies would be between 10 and 15.

Vibrational spectra of XeF$_6$ have been studied by Smith and Begun (5, p. 300) at Oak Ridge and by the author and co-workers (5, p. 304) (11). Figure 9.11 is a tracing of the infrared spectrum obtained at Argonne. Smith obtained a similar spectrum, but neither group was able to obtain reliable tracings at lower frequencies because of attack on all known transparent window materials. Begun found Raman scattering peaks at 655, 635, and 582 cm^{-1}. The author verified these peaks for the solid and also found Raman peaks at 579, 516, and 471 cm^{-1} for XeF$_6$ dissolved in liquid WF$_6$. These, however, were just barely above background and their existence must be considered as questionable. Hyman and Quarterman (5, p. 278) observed a Raman band at 620 cm^{-1} for XeF$_6$ dissolved in liquid HF.

These spectral data present an enigma, rather than a definite answer. One may cite the two infrared bands at 520 and 613 cm^{-1} as proof that the molecule is not highly symmetrical, since only one stretching vibration is allowed for the symmetrical model and only one is found for all the other hexafluorides. On the other hand, the yellow color of gaseous XeF$_6$ mentioned earlier means that the molecule has low-lying electronic levels. It is possible that part of the absorption between 500 and 600 cm^{-1} is due to electronic motions of unusually low frequency rather than to vibrational motions, and that the molecule is symmetrical. The two bands at 1230 and 1100 cm^{-1} are similar to combination bands, $\nu_1 + \nu_3$ and $\nu_2 + \nu_3$, observed for the symmetrical hexafluorides. The final answer will have to await the collection of more extensive data.

93

Efforts to obtain diffraction data for XeF_6 have all been plagued by the reactivity of the samples, and no structural determinations have yet been published.

Fluorine nuclear magnetic resonance chemical shifts for XeF_6 were 310×10^{-6} for the crystal and 309×10^{-6} for the liquid relative to the F_2 molecule (5, p. 252). No multiplet structure was found. A charge of $-0.4e$ on the fluorines was calculated.

9–E STRUCTURE OF $XeF_2 \cdot XeF_4$.

In the earliest report on the crystal structure of XeF_4, a second crystalline form was mentioned (7). This monoclinic form was later carefully analyzed by Burns, Ellison and Levy (5, p. 226). They found by x-ray diffraction analysis that the unit cell contained two molecules of XeF_2 and two of XeF_4, each molecule retaining its usual shape and size to within experimental error. This rather interesting material might be called XeF_3, but is more appropriately described as a molecular addition compound, $XeF_2 \cdot XeF_4$.

9–F STRUCTURE OF XeO_3.

The thermodynamically unstable crystalline XeO_3 was analyzed by x-ray diffraction by Templeton and co-workers (5, p. 229). Although crystals of this material frequently detonate with great violence, and though they always decomposed more or less rapidly in the x-ray beam, the experimenters persisted until they had measured intensities on 482 independent reflections. Because many different crystals had to be used in turn, one of the reflections (from the 200 planes) was used to adjust the data so as to make them comparable. The unit cell was found to be orthorhombic with dimensions of 6.163, 8.115, and 5.234 Å. Structure determination was facilitated by comparison with information available on the HIO_3 crystal structure. Xenon locations were very close to those of iodine in HIO_3. Locations of oxygen atoms were possible to an uncertainty of the order of 0.03 Å. A definite identity for the molecule was established since three Xe-O distances were equal, within the uncertainty, to 1.76 Å, and all other interatomic distances were greater than 2.8 Å. The XeO_3 molecules, within the uncertainty, were found to be symmetrical, triangular pyramids with the Xe-O bond length being 1.76 Å and the interbond angle being 103°.

The infrared spectrum of solid XeO_3 was reported by Smith (12) and the Raman spectrum of an aqueous solution was studied at Argonne (13). Figure 9.12 shows the Raman spectrum of the solution. The four most intense Raman bands are interpreted as due to undissociated XeO_3 molecules. Their frequencies correspond well with those of the four infrared bands of the solid. This indicates

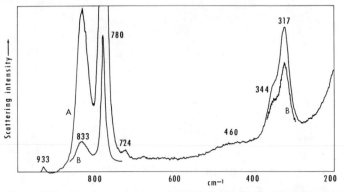

Figure 9.12 Raman spectrum of $2M$ XeO_3 in H_2O. From Ref. 13.

symmetrical, pyramidal molecules for both phases. Molecules of this symmetry (ammonialike) have four fundamental frequencies, all active in both spectra. Table IX.2 lists these frequencies, as well as those of two isoelectronic ions.

Table IX.2

Frequencies for Comparison

Molecule or ion	Method of Observation	ν_1	ν_2	ν_3	ν_4	References
$[TeO_3]^{2-}$	Raman of solution	758	364	703	326	(14)
$[IO_3]^-$	Raman of solution	779	390	826	330	(15)
XeO_3	Raman of solution	780	344	833	317	(13)
XeO_3	Infrared of solid	770	311	820	298	(12)

9–G STRUCTURE OF XeO_4.

The existence of XeO_4, and the shape of the molecule as tetrahedral (O nuclei at the corners of a regular tetrahedron) were predicted by Gillespie (5, p. 333) before anyone knew how to prepare it. Very recently the infrared spectrum of the vapor was observed at Argonne

(16). This is reproduced as Fig. 9.13. Because of difficulties with decomposition, several bands (marked with an X) of impurities show up. Only the two most intense bands in the spectrum are due to XeO_4. These data clearly indicate the regular tetrahedral shape,

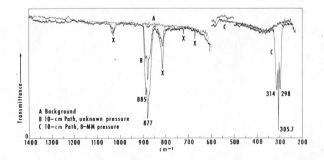

Figure 9.13 Infrared spectrum of XeO_4 gas. From Ref. 16.

since only for that symmetry would there be just two infrared-active fundamentals. Table IX.3 shows a comparison of frequencies with those of the isoelectronic $(IO_4)^-$ ion and of the similar OsO_4 molecule. The correspondence is as close as one might expect. From the

Table IX.3

Frequencies of Fundamentals for XeO_4, IO_4^-, and OsO_4

Molecule	ν_1	ν_2	ν_3	ν_4	Reference
XeO_4	?	?	877	305.7	This work
$(IO_4)^-$	791	256	853	325	(17)
OsO_4	971	328	960	328	(18)

P-R spacing of $16 \, cm^{-1}$ observed for the $305.7 \, cm^{-1}$ band it is possible to calculate a rough value of bond length. The result is $1.6 \, Å$ with an uncertainty of 0.1 or 0.2 Å for bond length in XeO_4. For comparison, XeO_3 solid has a bond length of 1.76 Å. No other structural studies have yet been reported for XeO_4.

9-H STRUCTURE OF METAL PERXENATES

Gruen (5, p. 174) studied the infrared spectra of hydrated and dehydrated perxenates of the sodium, silver, lead, and uranyl ions.

In addition to absorptions by water of hydration, carbonate impurity, etc., the important observation was an intense band in the 650 to 680 cm^{-1} region. This band was interpreted as the infrared-active ν_3 of an octahedrally symmetrical (XeO$_6$) group. A recent x-ray study of sodium perxenate (19) led to similar conclusions. A single crystal of Na$_4$XeO$_6$·8 H$_2$O was analyzed by x-ray diffraction, and found to contain (XeO$_6$)$^{4-}$ ions, approximately in the form of a regular octahedron. The angles found were not significantly different from 90°, and the Xe-O bond lengths averaged 1.875 Å. An x-ray study of the hexahydrate of sodium perxenate (20) led to similar results. The average of the Xe-O distances was 1.84 Å, and the deviations from the regular octahedral shape were considered to be within experimental uncertainty.

References

1. G. HERZBERG, "Spectra of Diatomic Molecules," D. Van Nostrand, 1950. G. HERZBERG, "Infrared and Raman Spectra of Polyatomic Molecules," D. Van Nostrand, 1945.

2. E. B. WILSON, J. C. DECIUS and P. C. CROSS, "Molecular Vibrations," McGraw-Hill, 1955.

3. D. F. SMITH, *J. Chem. Phys.*, **38**, 270 (1963).

4. P. A. AGRON, G. M. BEGUN, H. A. LEVY, A. A. MASON, C. G. JONES and D. F. SMITH, *Science*, **139**, 842 (1963).

5. "Noble-Gas Compounds," H. H. HYMAN, Ed., Univ. of Chicago Press, 1963.

6. H. H. CLAASSEN, G. L. GOODMAN, J. G. MALM and F. SCHREINER, *J. Chem. Phys.*, **42**, 1229 (1965).

7. S. SIEGEL and E. GEBERT, *J. Am. Chem. Soc.*, **85**, 240 (1963).

8. H. A. LEVY and P. A. AGRON, *J. Am. Chem., Soc.*, **85**, 241 (1963).

9. J. MARTINS and E. B. WILSON, JR., *J. Chem. Phys.*, **41**, 570 (1964).

10. J. H. BURNS, P. A. AGRON and H. A. LEVY, *Science*, **139**, 1208 (1963).

11. H. H. CLAASSEN, CEDRIC L. CHERNICK and J. G. MALM, *Abstracts of the Am. Chem. Soc. New York Meeting, Sept. 9–13* (1963), page 34N.

12. D. F. SMITH, *J. Am. Chem. Soc.*, **85**, 816 (1963).

13. H. H. CLAASSEN and G. KNAPP, *J. Am. Chem. Soc.*, **86**, 2341 (1964).

14. H. SIEBERT, *Z. anorg. U. allgem. Chem.*, **275**, 225 (1955).

15. S. T. SHEN, Y. T. YAO and T. WU, *Phys. Rev.*, **51**, 235 (1937).

16. H. SELIG, H. H. CLAASSEN, C. L. CHERNICK, J. G. MALM and J. L. HUSTON, *Science*, **143**, 1322 (1964).

17. H. SIEBERT, *Z. anorg. U. allgem. Chem.*, **273**, 21 (1953).

18. N. J. HAWKINS and W. W. SABOL, *J. Chem. Phys.*, **25**, 775 (1956).

19. W. C. HAMILTON, J. A. IBERS and D. R. MACKENZIE, *Science*, **141**, 532 (1963).

20. A. ZALKIN, J. D. FORRESTER, D. H. TEMPLETON, S. M. WILLIAMSON and C. W. KOCH, *Science*, **142**, 502 (1963).

CHAPTER **10**

Chemical Binding and Theoretical Descriptions
of Xenon Compounds

The possible energies of atoms, as noted in Chapter 3, can be precisely computed from the Schroedinger equation for one-electron atoms (H, He^+, etc.). For two electrons the problem is much more complicated and for atoms containing more than two, the rough approximation must be used of lumping all electrons but one together as behaving like a spherical charge cloud. Similarly, for the very simplest molecule, H_2^+, a precise solution for the single electron is possible if the nuclei are considered fixed. Again, the energies are quantized, and one expects that the electron will occupy the lowest possible energy level in the normal molecule. Each of the energy levels, however, is a function of the nuclear separation distance R. The Born-Oppenheimer (1) approximation then assumes that this energy, which includes both the potential and kinetic energies of the electron, may be identified with the potential energy that controls the relative motion of the nuclei. This approximation is a very good one because the nuclei are much more massive than the electron and move very slowly in comparison. It may be extended immediately to complicated systems and is included as a basic assumption in theoretical treatments of molecules.

Detailed treatments of the hydrogen molecule-ion may be found in most textbooks of quantum mechanics and will not be given here. The two nuclei are chemically bound by the one electron because the lowest energy level has a definite minimum when plotted as a function of R. This occurs at $R = 1.06$ Å and is about 2.7 electron volts below the energy for very large R. Figure 10.1 shows the four lowest energies as functions of R. Corresponding to any point on a curve there is a definite ψ function that determines the density of the electron cloud. As noted in Chapter 3, quantum mechanics does not define definite electron orbits for atoms, but gives only probabilities of electron positions. $|\psi|^2 \, dv$ is proportional to the probability of finding the electron in the volume element dv. The word, orbital, is commonly used to represent such a probability cloud in which an electron (or two electrons) moves. In Fig. 10.1, any point on curve a represents a bonding orbital. It is called bonding because curve a has a definite

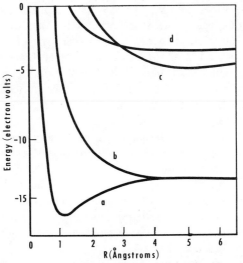

Figure 10.1 Lowest energy levels of H_2^+ as functions of R, the internuclear distance.

minimum. If the molecule-ion is in this lowest energy level, there is an attractive force between the nuclei if R is between 1.06 and (say) 4 Å, and there is a force of repulsion if $R < 1.06$ Å. For curve b, on the other hand, the force is always repulsive; if the electron is in this energy level it is in an anti-bonding orbital.

That a system of two positive protons and one negative electron can be bound together by an energy of 2.7 electron volts (about 100 times the thermal energy of an atom at room temperature) is rather amazing in view of the large Coulomb repulsion between the protons. Slater (2, p. 39) gives an intuitive description of this that we quote, "As two atoms come together from infinite separation, we know that if they are forming a covalent bond, an overlap charge is built up in the region between them. Let us now ask what is the force acting on one of the nuclei, as a result of this overlap charge, and the spherically symmetrical charges centered on both nuclei. The spherical charge centered on the nucleus on which we are finding the force will exert no force on that nucleus. The other nucleus, only partly shielded by its spherically symmetrical charge, will exert a repulsive force. But the overlap charge, whose average position is midway between the nuclei, will exert an attractive force on the nucleus in question, which will be large, on account of the short distance between nucleus and overlap charge. In the attractive region, where R is greater than the equilibrium distance, this attraction will outweigh the repulsion of the other nucleus, and we thus have the explanation of the net attraction in this region. As R becomes smaller than the equilibrium distance, the situation changes . . . the larger part of the charge is now located to the left of the left-hand nucleus, to the right of the right-hand nucleus. Each nucleus is then not only repelled by the other nucleus, but pulled away from the other nucleus by the attraction of the electronic charge which is, so to speak, behind it."

The importance of the overlap charge cloud density between the nuclei must be emphasized because it is essential in binding, and the idea is much used in qualitative and semi-quantitative descriptions of bonds between larger atoms. The term "overlap" is used since this part of the charge distribution in the detailed theory is calculated by means of an integral that contains the product of two atomic wave functions. The value of the integral depends on the amount of overlapping of atomic orbitals of the two nuclei, hence overlap integral, or overlap charge density.

The hydrogen molecule-ion discussed thus far is not an important molecule except for the fact that for it the quantum-mechanical equations can be solved accurately. For the next more complicated molecule, neutral hydrogen, the problem is so much more difficult that already approximations are necessary. Many different methods of approximation have been used by various workers and reasonable accuracies have been attained through a number of different approaches. The reader is referred to Chapters 4 and 5 of Slater's book (2) for discussions of the most important of these various methods. Many of the qualitative aspects of the one-electron bond carry over to the two-electron bond. The lowest energy state again has a pronounced minimum. It is a deeper minimum and occurs at a smaller distance (0.74 Å) between the nuclei than for H_2^+. The binding energy is 4.48 electron volts compared to 2.7 for the one-electron bond. The bonding orbital at the equilibrium separation is spread out in an ellipsoid with the largest electron density near the two nuclei and between them.

Molecules of interest usually have many electrons and more approximations are necessary in their theoretical treatment. Generally, most of the electrons of an atom in a molecule are lumped together as a spherical charge cloud or "core," and a few in each atom are considered as involved in the binding. The method of attack usually is similar to one of the methods that have proved successful for hydrogen. The most popular description of chemical bonds is called the valence-bond or hybrid orbital picture. It is primarily a qualitative description, and yet has had a wide success in predicting molecular structures, particularly for inorganic compounds. It is simple enough to allow one to form a mental picture of the nature of a chemical bond without detailed mathematical calculations. The method is limited, and does not lend itself easily to explanations of electronic spectra.

The valence-bond approach emphasizes localized electron pair bonds. The stationary shared pair conceived by G. N. Lewis (3) in 1916 has developed into a bonding orbital that places the main electron density or probability in the region between two atoms. It is formed when a half-filled orbital of the one atom overlaps a half-filled orbital of the other. Large volumes of overlapping correspond to strong bonds, and are possible when the atomic orbitals extend out in preferred directions in space.

As a simple example of how the valence bond method predicts shapes of molecules, we may consider the water molecule. The three 2p orbitals of oxygen extend along three perpendicular directions as shown in Fig. 10.2. One is filled but the other two are singly occupied.

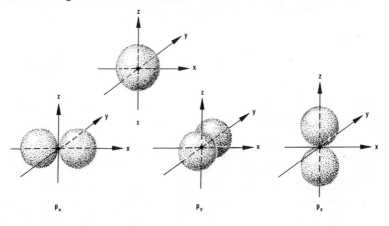

Figure 10.2 Approximate shapes of the 1s and 2p orbitals. The three p orbitals are directed along three perpendicular directions.

These two may be overlapped by the 1s orbitals of two hydrogen atoms to form bonds at right angles. Because the bonding electrons average somewhat closer to the O atoms than to the H atoms, the latter have a net charge and are pushed apart to the observed angle of 104.5°.

The simple picture of s, p, etc., orbitals must be extended to include hybrid orbitals. If ψ_s, ψ_{px}, ψ_{py}, and ψ_{pz} are wave functions representing the four s and p orbitals and satisfying the Schroedinger equation for the atom, then linear combinations of them such as $(a\psi_s + b\psi_{px} + c\psi_{py} + d\psi_{pz})$ are also solutions of the wave equation. It is possible to form a set of four different but equivalent linear combinations that are called sp^3 hybrids. Each of these orbitals extends primarily in one direction as shown in Fig. 10.3a, and therefore offers the possibility of more overlap and stronger bonds than does a p-orbital. The four equivalent hybrids extend toward the corners of a regular tetrahedron (Fig. 10.3b). For the second row of elements, d-orbitals are also available and a common hybridization gives six sp^3d^2 orbitals that extend outward toward the corners of a regular octahedron. Such a set is shown in Fig. 10.3c.

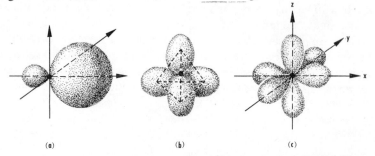

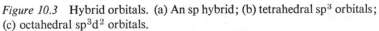

Figure 10.3 Hybrid orbitals. (a) An sp hybrid; (b) tetrahedral sp^3 orbitals; (c) octahedral sp^3d^2 orbitals.

For isolated atoms s, p, d, or f orbitals are energetically preferred, but the promotional energy to yield hybrids may be supplied in compound formation because this allows more overlap in the bonds. Thus, atomic carbon has four electrons in the $n = 2$ shell. Two are in the 2s orbital and there is one each in two of the 2p orbitals. For most carbon compounds, however, tetrahedral sp^3 hybrids are used. The water molecule may also be described in terms of four tetrahedral sp^3 hybrids, two of which are occupied by unshared pairs and two of which are occupied by shared or bonding pairs. This would predict an interbond angle of 109°, the tetrahedral angle. An empirical rule (4) says that repulsive forces between unshared pairs are greater than between shared pairs. Hence the angle between the two bonds is reduced to the observed 104.5°.

Although the noble-gas atoms after helium all have filled outer shells (s^2p^6) with all electrons paired, compound formation is not ruled out by the valence-bond concepts. The commonly quoted "rule of eight" is an out-of-date carryover from Lewis' (3) picture of static electrons at corners of a cube. The arrangement of eight electrons about an atom in a molecule is common, but so are other arrangements, such as that of twelve electrons in an octahedral configuration. Many ions that are isoelectronic with noble-gas-compound molecules exist in solution. For example, the ions S^{2-} and Cl^- each have 18 electrons in a configuration like that of an argon atom. Both are relatively easily oxidized to the common $(SO_4)^{2-}$ and $(ClO_4)^-$. These, except for the charge on the central nucleus, are like the hypothetical ArO_4 and similar to the known XeO_4 molecules. The dogma, generally believed by modern chemists until the recent discovery of xenon compounds, that the noble gases cannot form stable compounds, was not a theoretical prediction. In fact, halides of noble gases were predicted from theory by several chemists in the twenties and early thirties when the quantum-mechanical ideas about chemical bonds were being developed. These predictions resulted in a number of attempts to make krypton and xenon compounds. The failure of these attempts strengthened the dogma that lasted from the discovery of argon in 1895 to 1962.

The known compounds of xenon and krypton may be simply pictured in terms of hybrid orbitals. For the difluorides we count eight electrons from the noble-gas atom and one from each fluorine atom for a total of two shared pairs and three unshared pairs. Because of the rule of greater repulsion between unshared pairs, we predict that the two fluorine atoms will be opposite each other and the three unshared pairs will be centered at 120° to each other in the plane halfway between the fluorine atoms. Thus, the linear and symmetrical shape is predicted. For XeF_4, twelve electrons must be accounted for around the xenon atom. For this, the very common octahedral orbitals may be invoked with the unshared pairs opposite each other. This suggests that the fluorine atoms shoud be in a plane square configuration as, indeed, is the case. The difference between molecules of SnF_4, which are tetrahedral, and the plane molecules of

XeF_4 comes about, in these terms, because of the necessity to find room for four more electrons in XeF_4.

For XeO_4, we may consider both the xenon and the oxygen with tetrahedral sp^3 hybrid orbitals. The xenon orbitals are all filled but each may be overlapped by a vacant oxygen orbital to form a bond. The result is a tetrahedral molecule. For XeO_3 there are three pairs of xenon electrons shared with oxygens and one unshared pair, again in nearly symmetrical distribution. For $XeOF_4$ one of the unshared pairs of XeF_4 is shared by an oxygen, leaving the molecule almost unchanged otherwise, as is also found from the vibrational spectra.

Simple extension of these ideas to XeF_6 leads to a prediction of an unsymmetrical molecule. The six fluorine atoms would naturally go into octahedral symmetry as in other hexafluorides, but an additional unshared pair would certainly cause a distortion. Unsymmetrical sets of hybrids, such as this would require, are relatively rare, and Coulson, in his comprehensive discussion of bonding in xenon fluorides (6), cites the existence of XeF_6 as evidence for the inadequacy of the hybrid-bond model for these compounds.

It certainly must be admitted that this general approach is quite limited and incomplete. Its main virtue is its ability to predict molecular geometry. This it has done admirably for all the noble-gas compounds with the possible exception of XeF_6. At the time of this writing the structure of XeF_6 is still in doubt, and the hybrid-orbital prediction of a symmetry less than regular octahedral remains to be tested.

One of the criticisms that has been noted about this simple description of xenon fluorides relates to the high promotional energies required. For xenon atoms (Table III.3, Chap. 3), approximately ten electron volts is required to promote one 5p-electron to a 5d orbital. For octahedral sp^3d^2 hybridization, two would need to be promoted, and it is difficult to see how enough energy could be gained back by bond formation to yield stability for the molecule. For XeO_3 of XeO_4, where no promotion to d-orbitals is required, since sp^3 hybrids would seem to be adequate, one should from this viewpoint expect greater bond energies than for the fluorides. Instead, the experimental binding energy for the xenon-oxygen bond is considerably less than for the xenon-fluorine bond.

It is clear that if an accurate theoretical description of these polyatomic molecules is ever given, it cannot restrict itself to localized electron-pair bonds. Each electron is influenced to some extent by

104

the whole molecule and not by only one or two atoms. The day of such accurate calculations for any polyatomic molecule still seems far distant. Extension to molecules of the general method of Hartree for atoms, in which one electron is considered to move in the field of the averaged positions of the other electrons, neglects certain correlation effects between electrons. These effects may be large enough to make the difference between stability and instability of the molecule. An extensive calculation using the Hartree method was recently done (5) for the F_2 molecule. The computer time cost for this problem was of the order of one hundred thousand dollars. The theory yielded a force constant and bond length of the right order of magnitude, and probably also a reliable electron distribution, but predicted that the molecule would not be stable! This is noted to emphasize that chemistry is still very largely empirical. Progress is rapidly being made in theoretical chemistry, but all calculations still involve many approximations.

Numerous authors have discussed the nature of xenon-fluorine bonds in terms of molecular, or delocalized, orbitals, and Coulson (6) has written a review outlining the main approaches. Only a brief description of some of these theories and their results will be given here.

Rundle (7), Pitzer (8), and Pysh, *et al.* (9) emphasized the problem of high promotional energies for xenon. They also pointed out that the xenon 5s-orbitals are significantly lower in energy than the 5p-orbitals. Thus, from an energy standpoint, the 5p electrons are most easily available for bond formation. To a first approximation, then, the molecular orbitals are considered to be linear combinations of the atomic p-orbitals of xenon and of fluorine.

The general idea is most easily given for the linear XeF_2 molecule, with extensions to XeF_4 and XeF_6 continuing along similar lines. For XeF_2 there are three 5p xenon and two times three 2p fluorine orbitals, and a total of 16 p-electrons. Linear combinations of the nine atomic orbitals may be taken to give nine molecular orbitals. These are described as σ_g, σ_u, π_g, and π_u according to the symmetry of the wave function. A σ-orbital is one that is a figure of revolution about the molecular axis. A π-orbital is one that is symmetric with respect to reflection in a plane containing the axis. The g subscript refers to a wave function that has the same value at any two points opposite and equally far from the center of symmetry. The u subscript refers to a wave function equal in magnitude, but opposite in sign, at any two points opposite each other with respect to a center of symmetry.

Figure 10.4 illustrates how σ_u and π_u orbitals may be formed from overlapping of a linear F-Xe-F system. The figure represents two of the three p-orbitals of each atom. If the atoms were moved closer

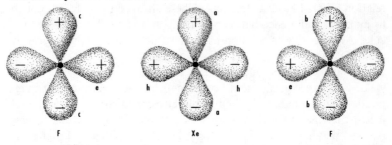

F   Xe   F

Figure 10.4 Atomic p orbitals used as a basis for describing molecular orbitals.

together the main overlapping would occur between the lobes marked h and those marked e to form a σ_u orbital. Some overlapping would also occur between the a-lobes and the b-lobes and between the a-lobes and the c-lobes. This would correspond to a π_u molecular orbital. Another π orbital equivalent to this would be formed from the p-orbitals perpendicular to the plane of the paper.

Three σ molecular orbitals could be formed from the three σ atomic orbitals,

$$\left.\begin{aligned}
\sigma_u &= F_\sigma + \lambda X_\sigma - F'_\sigma \\
\sigma_g &= F_\sigma + F'_\sigma \\
\sigma'_u &= F_\sigma - \mu X_\sigma - F'_\sigma
\end{aligned}\right\} \tag{1}$$

where F, X, and F′ represent atomic orbitals and λ and μ are constants chosen so as to minimize energy. To obtain orthogonal functions in terms of the three basis functions we must have $1 - \lambda\mu + 1 = 0$, or $\lambda\mu = 2$. Coulson estimated that $1 < \lambda < \sqrt{2} < \mu < 2$, and ordered energies $E(\sigma_u) < E(\sigma_g) < E(\sigma'_u)$. A similar set may be written for π orbitals

$$\left.\begin{aligned}
\pi_u &= F_\pi + \lambda' X_\pi + F'_\pi \\
\pi_g &= F_\pi - F'_\pi \\
\pi'_u &= F_\pi - \mu' X_\pi + F'_\pi
\end{aligned}\right\} \tag{2}$$

where similar inequalities will apply. These, of course, are doubly

106

degenerate since there would be a similar set in a perpendicular plane. Or, if they are considered together, each π orbital will have room for four electrons.

Figure 10.5 is an energy level diagram similar to that given by Coulson (6) showing qualitatively how the atomic energy levels are related to the molecular ones. In this approximation the five 2p elec-

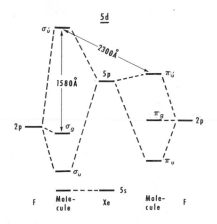

Figure 10.5 Qualitative energy level diagram for XeF_2 orbitals.

trons of each fluorine atom and the eight 5s and 5p electrons of the xenon atom (for a total of 18) must be placed in the molecular orbitals. Each of the σ orbitals can hold two and each of the π orbitals may hold four for a total of 20. The highest level, σ'_u, will therefore be vacant in the normal molecule.

It is the σ orbitals that are primarily involved in bond formation because they have a much greater possibility of overlap than do the π orbitals. To a first approximation, the charge transfer is related simply to the coefficient λ in Eq. (1). The σ'_u orbital is unoccupied and the σ_g orbital simply leaves the two fluorine electrons on the fluorines, but the coefficient, λ, determines what fraction of two more electrons is left in the xenon orbital. Specifically the fraction is $\lambda^2/(1^2 + \lambda^2 + 1^2)$, or the number of electrons in the xenon orbital is $2\lambda^2/(2 + \lambda^2)$ and on each fluorine is $2/(2 + \lambda^2)$. If $\lambda = 1$, the fluorine atoms each have a net charge of $-2e/3$, and if $\lambda = \sqrt{2}$ they have $-e/2$. Thus, the xenon atom is left with a deficiency of between 4/3 and one electron charges according to Coulson's estimate for λ. This points out the importance of the electron affinity of fluorine in these bonds and predicts the lower stability of krypton difluoride because of the greater ionization potential of krypton.

This scheme of linear $F - Xe - F$ with delocalized molecular orbitals made up primarily of atomic p orbitals has been extended in a rather straightforward fashion to XeF_4 and XeF_6. Thus, the plane-square structure of XeF_4 is explained, and an octahedral XeF_6 is predicted from the fact that the xenon 5p orbitals extend along three mutually perpendicular directions. The coefficient, λ, is expected to increase for the second and third linear set because of the increasing difficulty of pulling charge away from the xenon. Thus, the excess charge on the fluorine atoms is expected to be somewhat less for XeF_4, and still less for XeF_6.

Since both fluorine and two of the plentiful xenon isotopes have nonzero nuclear spins, the technique of nuclear magnetic resonance (NMR) has been used to obtain further data relevant to electron densities in the xenon fluorides. A spinning nucleus with nonzero magnetic moment will precess when in an external magnetic field. NMR techniques yield precise values of these precession frequencies and (since these are proportional to field strength) thus of actual magnetic field strengths at the nuclei. The magnetic field at a nucleus is less than the applied field because of diamagnetic (Lenz' law) shielding of the electrons. For atoms with spherical electron distributions this shielding field is calculable by means of a formula given by Lamb (10). It is proportional to the electrostatic potential at the nucleus due to the electrons and thus provides a relative measure of the number of electrons around a nucleus. For an isolated fluoride ion, F^-, for example, the shielding would be greater than for an isolated fluorine atom.

The shielding of the field is small compared to the applied field and one may define the shielding factor, $\sigma = \Delta f/f$, the change in precession frequency over the actual frequency. The Δf may not be measurable since one cannot observe the nuclei stripped of electrons, but a change in Δf may be measured relative to a standard chemical state and a relative or "chemical shift" listed.

Extension of these early ideas on shielding to a theory applicable to molecules is very complex and cannot be discussed here. A relatively brief discussion by Zimmerman (11) may be consulted for an introduction to this theory and for references to the literature. Hindman and Svirmikas (12) measured fluorine resonances for the xenon fluorides and oxyfluoride. The shielding constants relative to the F_2 molecule are given in Table X.1. Also given are calculated

Table X.1

Shielding Constants and Calculated Results According to Reference (12)

Compound	Shielding Constant Relative to $F_2 \times 10^6$	Charge on Fluorine atoms
XeF_2	612	$-0.7e$
XeF_4	482	$-0.55e$
XeF_6	310	$-0.4e$
$XeOF_4$	328	$-0.4e$

charges on the fluorine atoms based on the assumption of pure σ-bonds from p orbitals and a theory given in part by Saika and Slichter (13). These results on excess fluorine charge agree with the qualitative predictions discussed above. Measurements of xenon chemical shifts for these molecules and of fine structure due to coupling between xenon and fluorine nuclei through the bonding electrons have been made at several laboratories. The results have been discussed in some detail by Jameson and Gutowsky (14), who compared several theoretical models and found that a localized description using d hybridization for the bonding orbitals gives better agreement between calculated and observed xenon chemical shifts than a delocalized model without d hybridization.

Returning now to Fig. 10.5, we note that the σ'_u orbital is vacant in the normal XeF_2 molecule and it is possible to have transitions to this level if appropriate energies are supplied. Pysh, *et al* (9) obtained additional support for this delocalized molecular orbital model from observations of the ultraviolet absorption spectrum. An intense absorption centered at 1580 Å was assigned to the $\sigma_g \rightarrow \sigma'_u$ transition, an allowed transition according to selection rules. Its absorbance was found to be of the expected order of magnitude. Another much weaker absorption at 2300 Å was assigned as the transition, $\pi'_u \rightarrow \sigma'_u$. This is symmetry forbidden, but is made weakly allowed by vibronic coupling. The transition must go from the ν_2 vibrationally excited level in π'_u to the σ'_u level. Thus, the absorption intensity should depend on the temperature according to the population of the $\nu_2(213 \text{ cm}^{-1}$ above the ground state) level. Pysh, *et al* found that the intensity of the 2300 Å band did, indeed, increase with the temperature of the gas, as required by this interpretation.

Finally, it may be noted that it is probably true that there are more pages of theoretical descriptions of bonding in noble-gas compounds in the literature than of accounts of experimental studies of the compounds. The descriptions, however, are essentially "after-the-fact" explanations and have included very few predictions of importance. This serves as an excellent case to emphasize that chemistry still is very largely an empirical science.

References

1. M. BORN and J. R. OPPENHEIMER. A good discussion of the Born-Oppenheimer approximation and its justification by the Feynman Theorem may be found in Chap. 1 of Ref. (2).
2. "Quantum Theory of Molecules and Solids," J. C. SLATER, McGraw-Hill (1963).
3. G. N. LEWIS, *J. Am. Chem. Soc.*, **38**, 762 (1916).
4. R. J. GILLESPIE, *Can. J. Chem.*, **39**, 318 (1961); *J. Chem. Educ.*, **40**, 295 (1963).
5. A. C. WAHL, *J. Chem. Phys.*, **41**, 2600 (1964).
6. C. A. COULSON, *J. Chem. Soc.*, 1442 (1964).
7. R. E. RUNDLE, *J. Am. Chem. Soc.*, **85**, 112 (1963).
8. K. S. PITZER, *Science*, **139**, 414 (1963).
9. E. S. PYSH, J. JORTNER and S. A. RICE, *J. Chem. Phys.*, **40**, 2018 (1964).
10. W. E. LAMB, JR., *Phys. Rev.*, **60**, 817 (1941).
11. J. R. ZIMMERMAN, Chap. 4, "Methods of Experimental Physics," Vol. 3, "Molecular Physics," D. WILLIAMS, Ed., Academic Press, 1961.
12. J. C. HINDMAN and A. SVIRMIKAS, "Noble-Gas Compounds," H. H. HYMAN, Ed., Univ. of Chicago Press, 1963, page 251.
13. A. SAIKA and C. P. SLICHTER, *J. Chem. Phys.*, **22**, 26 (1954).
14. C. J. JAMESON and H. S. GUTOWSKY, *J. Chem. Phys.*, **40**, 2285 (1964).

CHAPTER **11**

Conclusion

At this point it may be expected that the author will indulge in speculations about future developments in noble-gas chemistry. He knows of no properties of the known compounds that will make any of them useful in, say, the kitchen or medicine cabinet of the home, but certainly a new field of inorganic chemistry is here to stay. How important this field will be, remains to be seen.

In the three years since XeF_4 was first described there have appeared in the scientific journals approximately 160 papers on noble-gas compounds. The intense interest in the new field is slowly moderating, and soon, new information on a compound of xenon will be no more interesting to the average chemist than similar information on a compound of an element such as tellurium.

When compounds of xenon were first announced in rapid succession one wondered whether hundreds of them might be produced in the future. Now, after three years, the only xenon bonds known are still those with fluorine or oxygen, the most electronegative elements. One is tempted to think that the essentials of noble-gas chemistry are already outlined and that future developments will be relatively minor. The author is not willing, however, to state this as a definite prediction; in the past, too many predictions of this kind have been quite wrong. It is still possible that a new development, such as a stable compound with a xenon-carbon bond, may open up a large new area in the field.

INDEX

INDEX

Adducts, 44f.
Analysis
  of aqueous xenon, 67
  of xenon fluorides, 40, 42
Appearance potentials, 55
Atmosphere, composition of, 5

Beattie-Bridgeman equation, 27
Bohr theory, 18
Boiling points of noble gases, 7
Bond energy
  in xenon fluorides, 53, 54, 57
  in xenon tetroxide, 56
  in xenon trioxide, 56
  predicted, 59
Bond length
  in xenon difluoride, 82
  in xenon oxidetetrafluoride, 91
  in xenon tetrafluoride, 89
  in xenon trioxide, 94
Born-Oppenheimer approximation, 98

Clathrates, 35
Clausius-Clapeyron equation, 50
Concentration of noble gases in the atmosphere, 5
Critical points of noble gases, 7, 13
Crystal structure
  of noble gases, 17
  of xenon difluoride, 84
  of xenon tetrafluoride, 91
  of xenon trioxide, 94

Density of noble gases, 7
Dielectric constants of noble gases, 7, 8, 9
Dipole moment, 8
Discovery of the noble gases, 1, 2

Electric discharge, preparations by, 46

Electrical conductivity of hydrogen fluoride solutions, 61
Electron diffraction of xenon tetrafluoride, 91
Energy levels
  of noble gas atoms, 24
  of the hydrogen molecule-ion, 99
  of xenon difluoride, 107, 109
Entropy of xenon tetrafluoride, 55
Equilibrium constants in xenon-fluorine system, 52

Force constants
  in krypton difluoride, 83
  in xenon difluoride, 83
  in xenon tetrafluoride, 86, 89
Free energy of formation, 55

Heat capacity of xenon tetrafluoride, 55
Heat of formation
  of xenon difluoride, 57
  of xenon hexafluoride, 57
  of xenon tetrafluoride, 55, 57
  of xenon tetroxide, 56
  of xenon trioxide, 56
  predicted values, 58
Heat of vaporization (sublimation), 31, 51
Hydrogen fluoride solutions, 60f.
Hydrolysis of xenon fluorides, 61f.

Infrared spectrum
  of heavy metal perxenates, 96
  of krypton difluoride, 83
  of metal perxenates, 96
  of xenon difluoride, 82, 83
  of xenon hexafluoride, 93
  of xenon oxidetetrafluoride, 90
  of xenon tetrafluoride, 85, 88

of xenon tetroxide, 96
of xenon trioxide, 94
Ionization of xenon
hexafluoride, 61
Ionization potentials of the
noble gases, 24

Krypton compounds, *see*
specific property, *e.g.* Infrared
spectrum

Mass, atomic, 5
Mass-spectrometric studies
of xenon, 41
of xenon difluoride, 41
Matrix isolation, 46
Melting point
of xenon fluorides, 42
of xenon oxidetetrafluoride, 43
Models of atoms, 8, 10, 11
Molecular structure
of hexafluorides, 92
of krypton difluoride, 83
of xenon difluoride, 79f.
of xenon hexafluoride, 92f.
of xenon oxidetetrafluoride, 91
of xenon tetrafluoride, 88, 91
of xenon tetroxide, 95
of xenon trioxide, 94
Molecules, diatomic, of noble
gases, 34
Mössbauer effect of xenon tetra-
chloride, 45

Neutron diffraction of xenon
difluoride, 83
Normal coordinates, 74, 75
of YZ_2 molecules, 81
of xenon tetrafluoride, 87
Nuclear magnetic resonance
studies
of xenon difluoride, 84, 109
of xenon hexafluoride, 94, 109
of xenon oxidetetrafluoride,
92, 109
of xenon tetrafluoride, 92, 109

Orbitals
atomic, 101

delocalized, 107f.
hybrid, 102f.
molecular, 105f.

Perxenates, 66f.
Platinum hexafluoride, 3
Polarization vector, 9
Potential energy, of atom pairs,
28f.
Potentials in aqueous solutions,
70
Preparation
of krypton difluoride, 46
of perxenates, 66
of radon fluoride, 47
of xenates, 65
of xenon fluorides, 38f.
of xenon oxidetetrafluoride, 43
of xenon tetroxide, 44
of xenon trioxide, 43
Properties
of krypton difluoride, 47
of perxenates, 67
of xenon fluorides, 42f.
of xenon oxidetetrafluoride, 43
of xenon(VI) solutions, 64f.
of xenon(VIII) solutions, 66f.
thermodynamic, 51

Quantum numbers, 19
Quantum theory for atoms, 18f.

Radii, atomic, 10f.
Radioactivity of radon, 48
Radon compounds, 48
Radon fluorides, 47
Raman spectrum
of krypton difluoride, 83
of xenic acid, 95
of xenon difluoride, 83
of xenon hexafluoride, 93
of xenon oxidetetrafluoride, 90
of xenon tetrafluoride, 85, 88f.
Ratio of specific heats
of argon, 2, 7
of krypton, 7
of neon, 7
Refractive index of noble gases, 7
Ruthenium hexafluoride, 3

Schroedinger equation, 18
Self-consistent field method, 20f.
Solubility in hydrogen fluoride
  of xenon fluorides, 60
Solubility in water
  of noble gases, 7
  of sodium perxenate, 66
  of xenic acid, 64
Source of supply of noble gases, 6
Structure: *see* Crystal structure
  and Molecular structure

Theory
  of chemical binding, 98f.
  of molecular vibrations, 71f.
  of Raman spectra, 77f.
Triple point of noble gases, 7

Ultraviolet spectrum of xenon
  difluoride, 109

Valence-bond theory, 102f.
Van der Waals equation, 12
Vapor pressure
  of krypton difluoride, 46
  of noble gases (elements), 32

of xenon difluoride, 42, 51
of xenon hexafluoride, 42, 51
of xenon tetrafluoride, 42, 51
of xenon tetroxide, 44
of xenon trioxide, 43
Vibrational spectra: *see* Infrared
  spectrum *and* Raman
  spectrum
Virial equation, 26, 29
Viscosity
  of noble gases, 7
  theory of, 14f.

Xenates, 65
Xenon compounds: *see* specific
  property, *e.g.* Infrared
  spectrum
Xenon-fluorine system, 51f.
Xenon hexafluoroplatinate, 3,
  37, 44
X-ray diffraction studies
  of sodium perxenate, 97
  of xenon difluoride, 83
  of xenon tetrafluoride, 91
  of xenon trioxide, 94